D1594251

TALES FROM UBERVILLE

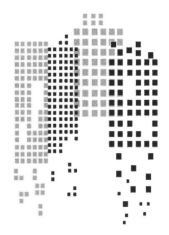

J.D. LAWSON

TALES FROM UBERVILLE

ISBN-13: 978-1-946203-43-4

ISBN-10: 1-946203-43-2

—Disclaimer—

Although the author and publisher have made every effort to ensure that the information in this book was correct at press time, the author and publisher do not assume and hereby disclaim any liability to any party for any loss, damage, or disruption caused by errors or omissions, whether such errors or omissions result from negligence, accident, or any other cause.

Paperback
Expert

www.PaperbackExpert.com

Table of Contents

Introduction..5

CHAPTER 1:
RUDE AWAKENING 9

CHAPTER 2:
THIRD-RATE ROMANCE.. 19

CHAPTER 3:
THE OCCASIONAL HICCUP 25

CHAPTER 4:
SUNDAY OUTING 31

CHAPTER 5:
A HELPING HAND.. 37

CHAPTER 6:
BLESSED 43

CHAPTER 7:
A TALE OF TWO STEVIES 53

CHAPTER 8:
MISTER MANNERS.. 61

CHAPTER 9:
CATWOMAN 67

CHAPTER 10:
FRAT BOY BLUES.. 75

CHAPTER 11:
MAIL-ORDER BRIDE 83

CHAPTER 12:
SURF'S UP! 95

CHAPTER 13:
JOSIAH 105

CHAPTER 14:
SOMEBODY'S DAUGHTER 111
CHAPTER 15:
FULL CIRCLE 119

Acknowledgements 125
Bio 127

Introduction

To quote Mick Jagger, "please allow me to introduce myself." That's as far as I'll extend the line because I am definitely not a man of wealth and taste. I am an ordinary Joe who, for about six months last year, drove for Uber and Lyft, the two well-known ride sharing companies that have achieved an impressive level of popularity in recent years. By itself, that makes me about as unique as a snowflake in the Rockies; recent estimates place worldwide Uber drivers at around three million and Lyft drivers at seven hundred thousand. Thus, what I did makes me a tiny dot on a statistical graph.

What may make me somewhat unique is my story and, more specifically, why I drove for Uber and Lyft. I'll start by saying that five years ago I would never have dreamed I would be working as an independent taxi service; I was far too successful for that (at least in my mind). By education and trade, I am a white-collar professional, a mediator and attorney at law with over thirty years' experience. But about a year ago, due to circumstances in and out of my control, I was an attorney and mediator with a daughter's wedding to pay for and a need for additional cash flow. A more detailed explanation of those circumstances isn't really necessary or relevant to this story. Just keep in mind that for those six months, by day I handled cases for clients and by night and weekends I drove folks wherever they needed to go. None of my friends or colleagues knew this. Only my wife did. And while I never picked up a client on a drive, I always knew the possibility existed that I would. That would have been awkward, I'm sure, but I figured I'd cross that bridge when I drove to it.

The city I drove (and currently reside) in is a fairly large one in the South. I have a family—the aforementioned wife and four children. We have a nice house in a nice suburban subdivision. We live a life that most would envy. We drive nice vehicles, we take nice vacations, and our children have never gone without the things they need and want. They're spoiled, but isn't that the American way?

My wife is also a very successful professional. So successful, in fact, that her income has nearly doubled mine in recent years. In today's world, that isn't supposed to matter, but every prideful bone in my body tells me that I am supposed to be the family breadwinner. That gnawing feeling had been eating away at my gut the past few years, and when we learned of our daughter's engagement and the scope of the wedding she wanted, I convinced myself that I needed to do more so that we wouldn't have to raid our retirement accounts. Driving for Uber and Lyft was the result. (Note: For purposes of this book, I will hereafter use "Uber" to collectively describe both services. Sorry Lyft; more people recognize Uber and use the word to generically describe all ride sharing services.)

Enough about me. This book is about the riders—those eclectic, eccentric folks who utilized my services from six o'clock until midnight during the week and as much as I could drive on the weekends. In just a few short months I saw it all: the good, the bad and the ugly. Driving was consistently rewarding, frus-

trating, humorous, heart-breaking, maddening and exciting—
sometimes all in one night. Rarely boring, always entertaining.

This collection of experiences and stories is also meant to be
entertaining, and I hope that the reader agrees. Oh, and everything you will read is 100% true. That's important because, as we
all know, the truth is always stranger than fiction. So, without
further ado, enjoy these Tales from Uberville.

CHAPTER 1:

RUDE AWAKENING

It's late afternoon on a Tuesday, and I'm driving into the great unknown. About a week earlier I made the decision to become an Uber driver. It took me several days to scour the website, get my documents in order, submit the necessary information and ultimately receive approval to begin driving. I drive a late-model SUV that has room for six passengers and reeks of comfort: heated leather seats, surround sound system, state-of-the-art climate control, the works. This automatically gives me a leg up on some of my competition, because some riders request a larger vehicle for a higher fare. I'm a little excited and a little nervous because, well, that's just the way you feel when you are dipping your toe in unfamiliar waters.

Part of the process of preparing to drive involves downloading the app. I may be in my late fifties, but even an old coot like me is now familiar with cell phone apps and how necessary they've become in so many aspects of our lives. Having a reliable cell phone and knowing how to use the app are critical if you want to be an Uber driver. Without this, you cannot receive a notification that you have a passenger to pick up, you cannot accept that request, and you cannot receive GPS directions for locating your passenger. I've spent much of the last couple of days familiarizing myself with all of this, so I begin day one with at least a small level of confidence that I can competently drive for Uber.

At precisely 5:30 p.m., I back out of my driveway and begin driving toward a popular commercial area not far from our neighborhood. I know that there are "hot spots" for drivers to hook up with riders and I assume this area will be one of them. It has a high concentration of hotels, restaurants and businesses, and I'm hoping that I can remain in the area and stay busy my first night. The plan is to try different areas my first week, testing to see which ones will prove to be the most fruitful.

About fifteen minutes into my new career, my cell phone pings and vibrates. I nearly jump out of my skin. It's a rider! He wants me!! I fumble with my phone, manage to press the right button, and in an instant I am headed to one of the nearby hotels with my magic carriage.

As it turns out, that first Uber trip is entirely uneventful. A businessman in town for the week needs a ride to a nearby restaurant. It's only a few blocks away and I know it won't be a monster payday for me. Nevertheless, I find my passenger, Mike, and greet him with a smile. He's a pleasant fellow and we visit the entire five-minute ride. I drop him off at the restaurant and just like that, I'm a veteran. Hey, this is easy! Then I look at my earnings for my effort: $2.96. Wow. That'll go a long way toward reestablishing my rightful place as family breadwinner. I immediately begin to have doubts about my new career choice.

The remainder of that first night is a mixed bag. I give a total of eight rides, all of varying times and distances. My enthusiasm rebounds and as the clock strikes 11:00 p.m. I see that I've earned almost fifty dollars. A few things become obvious throughout the night. Longer rides result in better earnings. Rides that take you away from commercial areas lead to down time because you spend time and miles driving back to the hot spot area without a passenger. Some passengers want to chat and others don't; it's pretty easy to recognize this within the first few seconds of the ride.

I debate whether to call it a night at that point and ultimately decide to wait for one more ride so I can break the fifty-dollar barrier my first night. Shortly after 11:00 I get the notification. I have a request from Amy, who is about ten minutes away in a part of town popular with twenty-somethings and millennials. This will be my first trip into that area tonight, and I am happy about it because it's an area I was planning to target later in the week anyway. The restaurants, clubs and bars stay open late and it seems like a natural area for ride sharing.

The destination to pick up Amy turns out to be all of the above – a well-known restaurant/club/bar in the heart of the neighborhood. I maneuver into a curbside parking spot very close to the front door of the establishment and wait. Waiting, I'm learning, is a part of the ride sharing process. Thus far on my first night I've had to wait on three or four riders, but the longest wait has been just a couple of minutes. Most folks are prompt. Those who aren't usually apologize and get to me as quickly as they can.

This ride will be different. I sense it almost immediately. Like a teenager walking through the forest on a foggy night in a horror movie, I know something is about to happen. And whatever it is, it probably won't be good. But I've accepted the ride, I'm here, and there's money to be made. I might as well make the best of it.

A hostess stationed outside the door of the club is staring at me. I know I'm probably not parked in a legal spot, but I figure it's used a lot by Uber drivers to pick up passengers coming out the door. I smile at her, as if to say, "I'm a new Uber driver; cut me some slack please." She frowns and looks back down at her table chart. Several patrons are milling around outside the place, and people are constantly going in and out. It's been over three minutes and Amy still hasn't revealed herself.

As the app instructs me, I call the phone number that's listed for Amy. She doesn't answer and my call goes to voicemail. So I text her: "This is your Uber driver. I'm outside the club waiting." No response. I consider leaving. The app allows you to report a no-show, but I'm sure Uber frowns upon driving away too soon and leaving customers stranded without a ride. For all I know Amy may be waiting in a bathroom line or paying her tab. I decide to continue waiting.

Just as my wait is about to hit the ten-minute mark, I decide it's been long enough. It's almost 11:30 and breaking the fifty-dollar mark suddenly doesn't seem so important. I turn on the ignition and give the club door one last glance. There appears to be a commotion. Four of the young persons who have been standing outside the entire time I have been parked begin walking toward me. A female taps on my front passenger window, so I roll it down.

"Hey! Are you my Uber?" She's screaming, and she's slurring her words.

"That depends. Are you Amy?"

Her face breaks into a huge, goofy grin. "YES! We need a ride home."

"What a coincidence. I'm here to give you a ride home. How many are in your group?"

"Four." Amy turns to her friends and gestures for them to get in. Counting Amy, there are two young men and two young ladies. The two guys climb into the captain's chairs immediately behind the front seats and the other female stumbles into the back bench seat. Amy sits in the front passenger seat, by me. "Mind if I sit up here?"

"That's fine. Whatever floats your boat." I notice that her head is bobbing and weaving. Either she's honing her defensive boxing technique or she's drunk, and I'm going with the latter. I start to pull away from the club, but before I do, I ask my standard departing question: "Everybody got their seat belts on?"

"I'm not gonna wear mine," the female in the very back announces. "It hurts my boobs." Thus begins the longest ten-minute ride of my life, to the posh condo development on the river where Amy or one of her companions apparently lives.

"Turn right! I know a shortcut," the unbelted female in the back blurts in my general direction.

"Shut up Becca. You don't even know where we are." I sense that Amy has little faith in her friend's navigational skills. "Turn left and it's a straight shot to where we're going. What's your name?"

"Jim. You're Amy, right?"

"Yep! And this is Steve and this is Peter." She points into the faces of the two guys behind us, who ignore her and continue their high decibel conversation about fantasy football. "And that's Becca in the back. She's drunk!" Thank you, Captain Obvious.

Right on cue, Becca confirms Amy's assessment of her. "I think I just threw up in my mouth!" Wonderful. The two guys turn to Becca in unison and warn her not to toss her cookies.

"Do I need to pull over for her?" I suddenly realize that from now on barf bags will come in handy when I drive.

The guy behind Amy speaks up. "No, she's fine. She always gets like this." I'm not reassured. As I'm having this conversation with Steve/Peter, Amy discovers my XM radio.

"I'm gonna find us some music!" I figure a happy rider is a tipping rider, even if she didn't ask for permission to commandeer my radio first. I immediately regret my decision not to stop her. She starts scanning the dial, but only after she has turned the volume up as loud as the system will allow. Without warning the glass in my SUV begins shaking violently and my eardrums begin to disintegrate. "WHERE'S KANYE! WHERE'S THE STATION THAT HAS KANYE MUSIC ON IT?" From this point, we only have conversation in all caps because it's the only way anyone can be heard.

"I DON'T KNOW. I MAINLY LISTEN TO SPORTS TALK SHOWS AND CLASSIC ROCK MUSIC!"

"THAT STUFF SUCKS! WHERE'S KANYE?" She frantically scans the band, at top volume, and has no success locating the elusive Kanye. As she scans, she decides to probe my musical taste. "DO YOU LIKE KANYE?"

I pause from trying to stop my ears from bleeding. "I'M NOT A FAN. I DON'T REALLY KNOW ANYTHING BY HIM AND I DON'T LISTEN TO THAT STYLE OF MUSIC."

Amy is incredulous. "I LOVE KANYE! HE'S THE GREATEST! I WANNA HAVE HIS BABY!" I look at Amy and immediately worry about the life choices she makes.

"ISN'T HE MARRIED? TO ONE OF THE KARDASHIANS?"

"YEAH. TO KIM. HE'S THE COOLEST!"

I decide to teach this young lady a thing or two about music. "HE'S A NO TALENT HACK AND A THUG. HERE, LET'S LISTEN TO SOME CREEDENCE CLEARWATER." I'm sure Kanye is very talented and far from a thug, but at this moment his biggest fan is starting to wear thin on me. I had been listening to "Bad Moon Rising" before this ride and I try to pry Amy's fingers from the scan button.

"NOOOOO!! HE'S AWESOME AND WE'RE GONNA LISTEN TO HIM!" Amy resumes her quest to find Kanye's voice on the airwaves.

"THIS IS A NICE RIDE, MAN! WHAT IS IT?" Steve/Peter is running his hands through the interior of the Enclave like a blind man reads braille.

"IT'S A BUICK ENCLAVE. THANKS. WE LIKE IT."

"A BUICK! YEAH, MY GRANDPARENTS HAVE ONE OF THESE." Steve/Peter must think I have one foot in the grave.

Becca comes back to life. "I JUST THREW UP IN MY MOUTH AGAIN! I HATE IT WHEN THAT HAPPENS!"

I glance back toward where Becca had been sitting and see that she's now on the floor between the two captain's chairs, with her head between her knees. Steve and Peter are staring at Becca, laughing at her current station in life. Dear Lord, please let this ride end.

"HAVE YOU EVER HAD ANYBODY VOMIT IN YOUR CAR?" I don't know if Amy is genuinely curious or if she is about to throw down a dare to Becca.

"NO, AND IF I HAVE MY WAY I NEVER WILL." I turn back to Becca's bowed head and plead as loudly as I can, "PLEASE TELL ME IF YOU NEED ME TO PULL OVER!" Silently, her head nods affirmatively.

Amy, resigned to defeat, settles on a Reba McEntire song that they all know and can sing along with karaoke style. The combined voices of Reba and four highly inebriated yuppies screaming at the top of their lungs is enough to wake the dead. Not surprisingly, no one but Reba can carry a tune.

"CAN YOU TAKE US TO ANOTHER CLUB?" Steve/Peter is apparently not ready to call it a night. I glance back at him in my rear-view mirror and shake my head no. "WHY NOT?"

"WELL, I GUESS I COULD, BUT YOU'D HAVE TO CHANGE YOUR DESTINATION ON THE APP. THAT WAY I GET PAID FOR TAKING YOU WHERE I ACTUALLY DROP YOU OFF." I hope the challenge of working Amy's phone app with blurred vision and poor muscle coordination will dissuade him from changing the route. I then get help from an unlikely source.

"NO! IF WE GO TO ANOTHER CLUB I'LL PUKE MY GUTS OUT!" Thanks for that mental image, Becca, and also for helping the group decide that enough fun has been had for one night.

After ten minutes that seem like hours, I find the condo and pull into a parking spot in front of the door. I resume command of the radio and turn the volume down to an acceptable level, but my ears are ringing and I'm sure I see hairline cracks in my windshield. "Well, we're here." The two guys empty out of the vehicle, neither offering to help Becca un-wedge herself from her spot on the floor between them.

I open my door, walk to one of the open rear doors and extend my hand to Becca. She looks at me like I just grew a third eye. "What are you doing?", she asks.

"You look like you could use some help."

"I don't need your help!" She wriggles and squirms, and after an awkward minute or two extricates herself from the vehicle. "See? Told you I could do it myself!" I marvel at how proud Becca is of this accomplishment.

Amy ends the night appropriately. Instead of a thank you, she turns to walk into the condo and mumbles in my general direction, "I'd tip you, but I spent all my money on drinks." I'm glad they made it to a home—safe, sound and somewhat conscious—but I can't help but wonder if this is a nightly routine for this crew. And I wonder what their parents would think if they knew how rudely their offspring were behaving.

As I park in my garage just before midnight, I realize I have been initiated. Welcome to the world of driving for Uber.

CHAPTER 2:

THIRD-RATE ROMANCE

It seems it's always the last ride of the night that sticks in my mind. I don't know why, except that my parents used to tell me "nothing good ever happens after midnight," and perhaps they were on to something. I'm toward the end of my first week of driving. It will be a short week, ending on a Thursday because we're going out of town this weekend. Around midnight I receive a notification to pick up a gentleman in an area of town with which I am unfamiliar. My wife always worries, and she constantly cautions me about staying away from unsafe and unfamiliar places. She means well, but what she doesn't understand is that if you want to make money driving for Uber, you accept all ride notifications and you do it before you really have an opportunity to determine where the rider is or where he or she wants to go. If you don't act quickly, the ride disappears. You are left wasting time and miles without a passenger.

That's the practical part of why I don't heed my wife's warning about my surroundings. The macho part is that I think I can handle myself wherever I might be, a foolish attitude if ever there was one. And the idealistic side of me tends to assume the best in people rather than the worst. Put all of that together and it means I drive wherever I have a chance to pick up riders, whether that's uptown, downtown, the 'burbs, the 'hood, or the unknown.

The last call tonight takes me to unfamiliar surroundings, to pick up Don. I can't tell from the address that shows on my app whether it is a residence or a business. Not that it matters, but that's just something that's nice to know as I approach a pick-up point. I see that I'm getting close, and the right side of the street is populated with strip malls. Strip malls are tough, because there may be ten businesses along one building and they might not all have street numbers on the doors. This particular strip mall looks challenging, mainly because all the lights are still on in every business. Don could be in any one of them.

And what a collection of businesses it is. A tattoo parlor, a couple of low-level bars, a genuine honky-tonk, an all-night laundromat, and a liquor store. I pull into an open parking spot and call Don. He answers on the third ring.

"Hello?"

"Hey, this is your Uber. Is this Don?"

"Yeah."

"I'm at this strip mall but I don't know where you are."

"Uh, drive around back. I'm by a dumpster behind the bar on the right."

Okay, fair enough. Who am I to judge Don's choice of pick-up points? I drive to the end of the strip mall, pull around to the back and see a large bearded man waiting. Thankfully he doesn't have a brown paper bag in his hand. I drive to him, put it in park and roll down my window. "Are you Don?"

"That's me. Say, we might have another stop on the way to my house. Is that okay?"

"Fine with me as long as it's not too far out of the way."

"It's not and I'll show you where it is." Don drops his cigarette, stomps it out, hops in and away we go. Five minutes later we arrive at a remarkably similar strip mall several blocks away, where a woman joins Don in one of the captain's chairs behind me. "Home, James!" Don laughs at his clever comment.

One of the things I'm beginning to pride myself on is my ability to make small talk with passengers when small talk is warranted, and to keep my mouth shut when I can tell my silence is appreciated. This is one of those times, but I cannot help but overhear the conversation. It's not as if they are whispering or trying to hide it from me.

"Hey baby. Did you get my message?"

"I did. But you have to stop sending messages on my cell phone. He checks my messages all the time when he sees my phone lying around."

"Then how the hell are you supposed to know when I want to see you?"

"I don't know. We'll figure something out. But I just don't want him seeing stuff like that on my phone."

Don laughs. "He didn't see those pictures I sent you, did he?"

"Lord no! I deleted those as soon as you sent them." Long pause. "Sometimes I think you want him to find out."

"Well sometimes I think you just don't want to see me."

Another long pause, followed by sounds that lead me to believe Don and his friend aren't brother and sister. Consciously avoiding my mirror now, the unmistakable sound of smooching is coming from behind me. After several seconds it stops and Don speaks again, only this time he's talking to me.

"Hey buddy, don't worry. We ain't gonna do anything in your car."

"Don't mind me. I'm just the driver." Chauffeuring these two illicit lovers around town in the wee hours of the morning isn't what I had in mind when I signed up for this gig. Thankfully, the romantic interlude is short and the conversation between the two resumes.

"What do you think he'd do if he knew what we're doing?"

She thinks for a second before answering. "Probably shoot us both with that new compound bow he bought at Bass Pro last week."

Don laughs again. "Hell, I was with him when he bought it!"

Ouch. So Don and the unsuspecting other guy are friends. This is getting worse—or better, depending on your perspective—by the minute. I'm getting the idea he's enjoying the danger in this as much as he's enjoying whatever the two of them are doing. I glance at my GPS directions and see that I'm very near the drop off point. "Excuse me, but don't let me drive past your house. I know I'm close."

"It's the third house on the left. And if you don't mind, I'm gonna add another destination for the trip. Hope you don't mind taking Beth home."

"Don't mind at all."

I stop in front of the white frame house and wait as the lip-locking continues. A few seconds later Don says his good-bye and walks toward his door. I finally allow myself to steal a glance in the mirror and I see Beth, staring out the window away from Don.

What do I say in a situation like this? Or do I say anything at all? I'm an Uber driver, not a counselor or a therapist. I don't make a habit of butting into other people's business. But boy, anybody can tell this train is headed off the rails and it won't be pretty when it happens.

We ride the remaining few minutes in total silence. When I finally get to Beth's place, she quickly opens the door, says "thank you," and disappears into her house. Once she's safely in, I set my course for home and turn up the radio. The song playing is one I remember from my youth in the 70s.

"Third rate romance. Low rent rendezvous."

How appropriate.

CHAPTER 3:

THE OCCASIONAL HICCUP

It's my second week as an Uber driver. I'm really getting the hang of this! Just like anything else in life, practice makes perfect. I'm well on my way to perfecting my driving secrets and methods. Dead zones have been identified, as well as a few surprising hot spots. I'm getting better with the app, so I'm not missing as many notifications; I'm accepting more rides as a result. And it may be my imagination—or maybe not—but I've learned that the absolute best way to ensure you will get a quick notification is to order something at a fast food drive-thru. Sure enough, once you've placed your order and are waiting to drive to the window, somebody will need an immediate Uber ride.

An integral part of being a well-oiled Uber driving machine is to know the best hours to be active. Because driving is not my main vocation, I've started structuring my day so that I do my real work from early morning until about 4:00 in the afternoon. I shut down at that point and begin driving so I can catch as many people needing rides home from work as possible. I can't always be that precise, but that's what I'm shooting for.

Occasionally, during my work day, I will use the lunch hour to run some errands. I may pick up some groceries, return some items for my wife at the mall, or run by the bank, the post office or the dry cleaners. It helps to break up the work day and it keeps me from falling into work ruts.

Today I've decided to go to an outlet store several miles from our home to look for a gift for my son. He's grown and about to take a ski trip with friends. When I asked if he needed anything, he said he could sure use some new snowboard pants, because the pair we gave him years ago doesn't fit anymore. I know the outlet store usually has some good bargains on things like that, so just before noon I shut off my computer and head to the store, which happens to be located in one of my Uber hot spots.

As I'm about halfway to the store, I think "what the heck." I open my Uber app, go online, and make myself available to pick up riders. Since I'm going to be out and about for an hour or two, why not make a little coin while I'm at it? I'm all about killing two birds with one stone.

Just before I get to the outlet store, the cell phone buzzes and I accept the ride. I look at the pick-up point and see I'm just a few blocks away. Great! Maybe the rider doesn't need to go far and I can still do my shopping after I drop him off. I make a slight detour and find the house.

Myron doesn't come right out so I call his phone. He answers, and it sounds like he just awakened from a deep sleep. That's strange since he just called for an Uber less than five minutes ago. He tells me to give him a couple of minutes and he'll be right out. True to his word, Myron emerges from the house and sits in the captain's chair behind me.

"You're Myron, I hope? Where are we going today?" I can always just look at my phone and know where we're going, but I like to ask anyway.

"Uh, there's a clinic over on Maple. I've got to pick up some medicine there."

"Okay. I'll have you there in just a few minutes." I look back in the mirror. Myron doesn't look so good. It's probably 65 degrees outside but he's wearing a heavy coat and a wool hat. He has his arms wrapped around himself like he's shivering. My astute medical training tells me something's amiss here. "You okay back there?"

A shaky voice replies. "Yeah, I'm good. Just need to get my medicine."

It's hard not to wonder what's going on with people, especially when you spend hours a day driving them around town. Myron is sick, and my mind starts to run wild. I wonder if it's contagious? What is the Uber protocol when a passenger dies in your car? Is he the subject of a government medical experiment gone horribly wrong? I'd love to know, but HIPPA laws and my own good sense prevent me from asking.

"HICCUP!" The sound startles me. It seems Myron has the hiccups. That's fine; we all get the hiccups. No big deal there.

"HICCUP!" This one is louder than the first one. It almost isn't a hiccup, sounding more like internal organs being reorganized in Myron's body.

"Are you sure you're okay back there?"

"Yeah, I'm okay. Just need to get my medicine. HICCUP! Excuse me."

"No problem. Hey, I know the hiccups are hard to get rid of sometimes." I wonder if I have a paper bag he can breathe in and out of. Maybe I should suddenly turn around and shout "BOO!" Anything to help out this poor fellow. It's the first time I've ever heard hiccups sound positively painful.

"HICCUP!" I actually catch a glimpse of this one and, I swear, Myron's whole body convulses as he hiccups. It hurts me just to see it occur, and I think Myron realizes it. "Man, I'm sorry. It's just that this medicine does all kinds of weird stuff to my system. It's bad on my intestines, but I've got to have it."

"Don't worry; I'll get you there, buddy." Am I an Uber driver or an ambulance driver now? Is there such a thing as a fatal case of the hiccups? He's been doing it non-stop for over five minutes, and they're coming faster and stronger by the second. I'm worried that if I look in the mirror again I might see his spleen coming up. "Can I get you some water or something?"

"No. Don't stop; just keep going. We're almost there. HIC-CUP!"

The clinic is in sight. Only four blocks to go, or eight hiccups, depending on your point of reference. And what kind of clinic is this anyway? On second thought, I'm not sure I want to know. We're here. Thank the Lord, we're here.

"You need any help getting in there, Myron?"

"No thanks. I'm good from here. HICCUP!" Wow, that one nearly took him to his knees.

Myron enters the clinic. I head home to Google "medicine hiccups side effects," hoping with all my might that it doesn't bring up Bubonic Plague, leprosy or something similar. On the bright side, this job gets more educational by the day.

CHAPTER 4:

SUNDAY OUTING

Fifty-seven-year-old men aren't supposed to be emotional or sentimental. It says so right on the back of the Man Card we all carry in our wallets. Somehow I've managed to hide from my family and friends the fact that I often have trouble following that particular code. Old Yeller made me cry as a child, and Field of Dreams tears me up even now. Heck, when Maximus dies at the end of Gladiator, or when Red crosses the Mexican border and sees Andy on the beach in Shawshank Redemption, I'm a blubbering mess.

I tell you this because driving for Uber does not immunize you against feeling sentimental at times. Today is Sunday, the first Sunday that I've been out driving for money, and I'm surprised at how busy I've been so far. Lots of folks are needing rides to the airport—going home after a family visit or hitting the road on business. It's been steady today, but by late afternoon I find myself in an area that my wife would describe as a bad part of town.

That's no problem, except I probably won't pick up any riders here. And just as I say that, the phone pings. Carl needs me!

I don't recognize the address that shows up on my phone but that's okay. I follow the route and it leads me to a heavily fenced public housing project. I drive into it and begin winding down the narrow streets and alleys. As I do, I take in what I'm seeing on both sides.

Human nature leads us all to certain prejudices and stereo-types. Even if we claim to be enlightened to the highest degree, we are human. We cannot help but have preconceived notions about people based on where they live, what they do, the color of their skin, or their socioeconomic status. It's wrong and I hate that that's the way we are, but it's true. If anybody tries to tell you differently, they are either lying or being naive. So as I meander through the housing project, I automatically begin thinking of poor welfare moms, minorities, drug pushers, crime, gangs and thugs. I hate that my mind gets cluttered with those thoughts, but it's happening as I'm observing my surroundings. I naturally assume that Carl will fit this stereotype, and I will be aiding and abetting a felon by transporting him to his dealer. In fact, the money he uses to pay Uber will probably be drug money. Will it be sufficiently laundered by the time my percentage is deposited in my account?

I pull up to the apartment with the number that is shown on my phone, and they are on the steps in front of their door, wait-ing on me. It's a family—a man, a woman, and two little boys. I roll down my window and ask, "Are you Carl?" The response I get from the man is a respectful, "Yes sir." Carl opens a back door and the younger of the two boys, who looks to be about six, goes to the back. The woman then sits right behind me and Carl sits beside her. The other boy, who is a couple of years older than his brother, sits in the seat beside me. I punch the button indicating that I've picked up my passengers, and the destination appears. We're going to Chuck E. Cheese.

Mom and Dad appear to be fairly young, probably early thirties. They are well dressed and quiet. The two boys, while obviously excited to be going to Chuck E. Cheese, are unusually well-behaved. Since the drive will be about fifteen minutes, I decide to break the ice. I turn to the older boy beside me. "What's your name?"

"Shawn. And that's my little brother, Demarcus, in the back."

"Well, my name's Jim and it's nice to meet you." I look in my mirror. "Hi Demarcus."

"Hello!"

"So, is it somebody's birthday today?"

Shawn answers. "No sir. I got all A's on my report card and my dad promised me we'd get to go to Chuck E. Cheese if I did."

"That's awesome. Where do you go to school?"

"Treadwell Elementary."

"Cool. Do you know what you want to be when you grow up?"

"Yes sir. I want to be a vet."

"Well you'll have to keep on making good grades if you want to do that. Why do you want to be a vet?"

"Because we had a dog and he got sick and died. We took him to the vet but we couldn't afford what he said it would cost to make him well. And when I'm a vet I'm gonna make all the sick dogs well for free."

Red just crossed the Mexican border. Ray Kinsella is having a catch with his dad. My eyes tear up as I hear this from Shawn. I glace back at Mom and Dad; they are both smiling at their son.

"Shawn, that's about the neatest thing I've ever heard. But you do know, if you do all that for free you won't make any money yourself?"

"Oh, I know. I mean I just won't charge the people who can't pay. I mean, their dogs are just as special to them as rich people and their dogs." Wisdom and truth from the mouths of children.

"Well, I think that's great. Hey Demarcus, how about you? What do you want to be?"

A high-pitched voice yells from the back, "I want to be a truck driver like my daddy was before he got hurt!"

Mom interrupts. "Demarcus, keep your voice down. You shouldn't yell in the car."

"I'm sorry momma."

My mind is wandering again. The picture in my mind is that of a father who has always worked and wants to work, but can't. Mother is supportive but can't do it all herself. Circumstances have put them where they are, but it's clear they are doing what they can to rise above it and raise their boys the right way. Maybe I'm off base but I don't think so.

We drive the rest of the way without much being said. Chuck E. Cheese is now in sight and the boys press their noses to the window glass, unable to contain their excitement. I get to the front of the restaurant and dad gets out and opens the door for the others. All four give me a sincere, "Thank you." Carl shakes my hand as he tells Shawn, "Hold your brother's hand 'til you get inside." Then he closes the car door and takes his wife's hand.

I want to do something for these people. I want to tell them their ride is on the house. I want to open my wallet and tell them that the pizza and games are complimentary today, courtesy of the Uber driver. I want these boys to have all the things they want and need. I want mom and dad to know that their efforts are noticed and appreciated. I guess more than anything, I want them to know that they are good people and they deserve more than life is currently giving them. But I don't do any of that; I just drive away and wipe my eyes with my sleeve.

And as I drive away from that part of town and the housing project, I curse myself for stereotyping. Nothing good ever comes from it, and as I've just proven to myself today, chances are you're dead wrong when you do it.

I hope the pizza is great and the games are all fun today. And when Shawn opens his vet clinic someday, I hope all the dogs he treats will get well.

CHAPTER 5:

A HELPING HAND

The website for Uber drivers provides helpful hints on how to make the experience more pleasant for riders. Among them are taking a small ice chest of chilled water, keeping things like umbrellas and Kleenex handy, and having a variety of music available on your radio. I know all of those things are appreciated, but for my money the best thing for making a passenger comfortable is just good old-fashioned courtesy. I try to be pleasant, polite and helpful all the time, even when some passengers make it difficult.

Lonnie is easy to get along with and I have no problem being polite to him. It's a couple of weeks before Christmas, and Lonnie is out late doing some shopping for his wife, family or friends at the all-night Walmart. I'd estimate Lonnie is in his early twenties and he has a shopping cart overflowing with things he's just bought, including toys. Lonnie must have a little one at home.

Like so many riders I pick up, Lonnie probably doesn't own a car, or at least he doesn't have one available when he needs it. He probably Ubered to the Walmart a couple of hours earlier and now needs a ride home. Once I make contact with him and figure out the door he's near, I see him and his carts full of stuff waiting to get out of the cold.

My vehicle has quite a bit of storage room, but one look at Lonnie's carts tells me I'll have to fold the captain's chairs down to create extra space. As I'm doing that, Lonnie begins emptying one cart and filling the rear space.

This is where my natural enthusiasm comes into play. Lonnie's been hard at work buying for people he cares for, so the least I can do is offer to lend him a hand. Several items in his other cart are large, and the clock is ticking on his fare.

"Hey, do you need a hand with some of your things?"

"Yeah, I appreciate it. I bought more than I thought I would when I came. I hope we can make it all fit."

"No problem. I'll make sure we get it all in." I pride myself on my packing prowess and organizational skills. "I'll get these storage things."

A quick scan of the situation reveals that Lonnie bought several of those large plastic storage bins with the lids that are supposed to snap tight on the top. It looks like three bins stacked inside each other, with the three lids sticking out the top. There's no way they'll fit in the back since Lonnie is already almost out of space there. The only other option is through one of the side doors, on top of a folded down captain's chair. I grab the storage bins and carry them to the open door behind my driver's door. No luck. The bins are as wide as the opening for the door, and those pesky lids are higher than the ceiling of my back seat area.

Undeterred, I turn the bins sideways, which causes the lids to fall to the pavement below. Oops. I shoot a glance at Lonnie, who hasn't even noticed what I'm doing. I pick up the lids and put them back in the bins, then I reassess the situation. It looks like if I put a corner of the bins in first, I can then twist them and they will fit. And to prove just how smart I can be, I place the lids flat across the top of the bins, thus creating more space for everything to fit. I'm a genius.

Everything goes according to plan until I tilt the bins upward to slide the bottom into the opening. It seems that the top lid has been knocked ajar from the other two, so that it's now wedged between the other lids and the car ceiling. I gently push but it won't give. Dang! That's the only thing that is keeping the whole load from being inside the vehicle. I look back at Lonnie, who has finished loading the rest in the back and is observing me with a cautious eye. I view his apparent skepticism as a challenge. No inanimate object is going to get the best of me.

The bins are plastic. Plastic is pliable. Really cheap plastic like the grade used to fabricate these bins is really pliable. If I just push a little harder, that contrary lid will bend a little more and slide on in the car. Just a little more push is all I need.

SNAP!!

It's a sickening sound and my heart sinks. I look up and the protruding lid is no longer wedged against the car ceiling. It is on the car floor…and on the asphalt…and in the car set…and just about everywhere. Shards of sharp pointed plastic have rained down from above, leaving one of Lonnie's bins totally topless.

On the bright side, everything else is now in the car.

"Oh my gosh, I am so, so sorry. I can't believe I just did that."

"Don't worry about it. It's no big deal."

I look at Lonnie and he sure doesn't seem as worried about it as I do. But doggone it, I just broke something that he bought. I feel horrible.

"Look, how much was that?"

"I don't know, but please don't worry about it."

"No, it's not right. How much did one of those bins cost?"

"I don't know; maybe ten dollars?"

I look at the bins and although I'm sure they didn't cost much, Lonnie did spend his hard-earned dollars on them, and for all I know they were the only dollars he had to spend at Wal-Mart that night. It's late, I'm ready to go, I'm sure Lonnie is ready to get home, and going back in Wal-Mart to buy a lid just doesn't seem like the thing to do. Besides, his Uber clock is running and it's not his fault that it is. I pull out my wallet and remove a crumpled ten-dollar bill.

"Here, please take this. It's the least I can do. I feel terrible about all this."

"No, that's too much. The whole bin cost maybe ten dollars; the lid probably doesn't cost half that."

"I don't even know if you can buy the lid without buying the bin too, so here, take the ten dollars."

Lonnie looks at my hand holding the currency and seems to be genuinely wrestling with whether to accept it. To help him make a quick decision, I stick it in his hand and close his fingers around it.

"I still think that's too much."

"Then just consider it a little extra for your trouble. Your Uber driver isn't supposed to break your stuff."

"Accidents happen, you know? You really don't have to do this."

"Yes, I do. I won't feel right if I don't."

Lonnie nods his head and gets in the vehicle. We drive the ten or so miles to his house in total silence. Even after giving him the money, I still feel awful about this. It's all I think about until I pull up to the curb in front of his tiny frame house. "Okay, we're here. Can I help you unload?"

"No, thank you." His response comes a little too quickly. We both laugh.

"Well, at least let me get your sacks for you." I carry a handful of plastic sacks full of little toys and before I get to his front door, a young woman opens it for me with a smile.

"Thank you for giving Lonnie a ride home. Our car isn't running, and we don't have many more opportunities to shop for Christmas."

"It's my pleasure, and I need to let you know I accidentally broke one of his storage bins."

Lonnie calls to her from the back of the car, "Just a lid. Not the whole bin."

I look at the young woman, who is still smiling. "I gave Lonnie some money to pay for it, but I'm so sorry for the trouble."

"It's no trouble at all, and you didn't need to give him any money for it."

As she is saying this, Lonnie walks up behind me and stuffs the ten-dollar bill in my jacket pocket. "How you gonna make any money driving if you just give it all back to the people you haul?"

"Well, I can start by being more careful with their stuff. And besides, it's not all about making money. At least part of it is about getting people where they need to go." Okay, so I fib about that just a little, but it sounds good.

Lonnie shakes his head. "Well, I appreciate it." He extends his hand toward me. Just before I shake it, I put my own hand in my jacket pocket, so that when I shake his hand the money passes between us one last time. He smiles. "You just don't take no for an answer, do you?"

"Not for something like this. Please, take it."

"All right, if you insist. Have a great night, okay?"

"You too. And Merry Christmas, ma'am."

"Merry Christmas to you too."

I drive away. When I reach a stop sign, I check the app on my phone to see how much I earned for that last ride. $8.62.

Lonnie was right; I won't make any money at this rate. But on account of my own stubbornness and stupidity, I figure paying $1.38 to give a nice man with Christmas gifts a ride home from Wal-Mart after midnight is a pretty good deal.

CHAPTER 6:

BLESSED

When you sign up to drive for a ride-sharing company, part of your "training" is to read information on the website pertaining to legal obligations. One of those is the driver's obligation to be non-discriminating toward riders, specifically including the handicapped. In other words, if a rider has a service dog, you can't refuse him or her a ride because you're scared Fido will poop in your car. That's just an example, but the point is that when you agree to drive for Uber, you are basically agreeing to give rides to anyone. Personally, I've got no problem with that at all, but I know there are folks who probably do. To each his own.

It's the weekend and I'm out fishing for riders on Saturday morning. My wife is out of town tending to family matters, so I figure I'll get an early start and see just how busy I can be – and how much money I can make – if I put in something close to a full day. Up to this point I've driven late afternoons and nights, but never a complete day. Today I'm going to change that.

Around 11:00 a.m. I get a notification that Charles needs a ride somewhere. Charles is in an area very near the airport, but it's a residential area so I doubt he's traveling. It's a modest but nice neighborhood and his house is easy to find. I park in his driveway and call to let him know I've arrived. After the third ring someone picks up and says, "Hello?"

"Is this Charles?"

"Yes, it is."

"This is Jim, your Uber driver. I'm in your driveway."

"Okay. I'll be around in a couple of minutes."

I hang up and begin waiting. Five minutes. Then ten minutes. I'm tapping my fingers on the steering wheel, wondering if I should report it on my app as a canceled ride, but I decide to call Charles again. As the phone is ringing, I notice someone is walking slowly toward my vehicle from the back of the house. I assume it's Charles, but confirmation is required so I roll down my window and speak in his general direction. "Charles?"

He pauses and cocks his head toward me, sunglasses shading his eyes from the bright morning sun. "On my way. Sorry for the wait; I couldn't find my earpiece." Bluetooth. Such a marvel of technology.

Hey, it was only ten minutes and I'm getting a few cents for the wait time, so it's not a big deal. But as Charles fully emerges from behind the waist-high fence that separates his front and back yards, I understand the reason for the delay. Charles is walking slowly, picking his way toward me as he rhythmically taps his red and white striped stick in front of him.

Charles isn't shading his eyes from the sun. Charles can't see the sun. He's blind.

I immediately open my door and jump out of the car. "Here, let me get that for you," I exclaim as I open the passenger door and wait for him to get there. I'm not sure but I think my voice is an equal mix of over-anxiousness and uncertainty.

"Thank you. I've got one earpiece in, so I can hear you okay, but seems like I always misplace the other one."

Charles isn't just blind. He's deaf too.

"That's okay; I'm ready when you are so take your time."

Charles smiles as he feels for the open door and shifts his body around so that he can hold the top of the door frame as he slowly settles toward where the passenger seat should be. When he's found it, he places the cane in his lap and feels for the shoulder strap. I watch all of this, wondering whether I should offer to help.

"Can I give you a hand with that seat belt?"

"Thanks, but I've got it." He snaps the metal end of the strap into the plastic catch protruding from beside the seat. "Nice car you've got here. What is it? A Buick?"

"Sure is. It's a 2017 Enclave we've had for about a year." I study Charles before I turn the key in the ignition, assuming he must be able to see at least a little.

Charles has probably had this conversation thousands of times before, so he answers my question before I can even decide if it would be rude to ask it. "I can't see at all. But my daughter and son-in-law have one of these, and I can tell from the feel of the interior. And I knew it couldn't be very old. It still has some of that new car smell to it."

The Enclave is a year old and I stopped smelling the new car smell about eleven months ago, but then I'm not Charles. Just as

I start to roll forward on the street, I notice that Charles drops something.

"Dang it!" Charles's hearing aid for his left ear has fallen between his seat and the console beside him as he tries to adjust it in his ear. The area where it's fallen is deep and narrow, and even I have trouble retrieving things that fall into it. I brake and park.

"Let me get that for you." I run my hand down along the floor beside his seat and feel the earpiece. After a couple of failed attempts, I manage to get a grip on it between my middle and index fingers and slowly bring it up from its resting place. "I hope it's not covered in French fry grease now."

Charles laughs a hearty laugh. "There ain't no telling where all this thing's been. Dang things just don't fit in my ears like they used to." I look closely, and it's obvious the hearing aides are not the latest models. In fact, they look downright antique. "I can actually hear a little out of my left ear, but the right one is just dead as a door nail. Say, do you mind if we listen to the game while we go to my sister's house?"

"Of course not. I was listening to it before I got here, and I just turned it down when I called you." I fumble with the volume knob and turn up the sound pretty high. "Is that okay?"

"You can turn it down some. I can hear just fine with the earpiece in. Most folks still talk real loud to me, but they don't need to." Embarrassed, I turn the radio back down to a normal level.

For the next ten minutes we talk football. Charles knows as much and apparently loves the game as much as I do, which is saying something, and it's all the more remarkable since he can't see anything. But our conversation is easy and enjoyable. He's a student of the game and he has opinions about everything, most of which are consistent with mine. I want to know more about what led to his blindness and deafness, but my genuine curiosity is balanced by my recognition that some folks are private and would rather not discuss such things with strangers. I respect that. Once again though, Charles's senses are spot on.

"You know, I wasn't always like this. In fact, I played football in high school and might have had the chance to play in college if I hadn't gotten drafted. Grambling actually offered me a scholarship."

"Well, you look like an athlete, so that doesn't surprise me."

Charles turns his head toward me and laughs again. "Now how can you tell an old broken-down fella like me used to play ball? I'm almost seventy years old."

I'm glad Charles can't see my embarrassment. "I can just tell. You just have that look about you, and you've still got that passion for it too."

"Well, I guess I was pretty good back in the day. 'Course the good colleges back then didn't let us black guys in, but I know I could've played for them big schools. I was pretty fast back then. I was all set to go to Grambling until I got my draft notice."

Charles had opened the door to the topic, so I go ahead and jump in. "So what happened to you?"

"Vietnam. That's what happened to me. Stepped on a mine in a field not too far outside Saigon in 1969. Haven't seen a thing since that day, and can't hear much of anything either."

"I'm sorry. But hey, I guess you were lucky it didn't kill you or affect anything else."

Charles doesn't correct me. Instead he just slowly takes the cuff of his pants and lifts his pants leg up, exposing a crude prosthetic leg. It's not a state-of-the-art leg like Lieutenant Dan's; it's a discolored wooden leg that probably belongs in the Smithsonian.

We drive in silence for a few seconds. I marvel at the attitude of this man who gave so much at such a young age for his country. Life isn't fair for many folks, no one more so than Charles. He says, "I still got scars that look bad, but you can't see them under my clothes."

"Do you get VA benefits? I mean, I hope you're getting taken care of by the government."

"Oh yeah, the VA pays for my earpieces and my canes and such. Bought me this leg to replace the original one back in eighty-eight. But I don't get to choose anything. They just give me what they think I need and send me on home."

I think back to the house where I picked up Charles. It was a nice house, very neat and well cared for. "Do you live by yourself?"

"Yeah. My wife passed about six years ago. My kids wanted me to move into one of them homes for the elderly, or maybe try to find a VA permanent place for me. But I ain't no invalid. I get around pretty good for a one-legged blind man." He grins as he says this.

"Amen to that. I'd say you're doing pretty well, all things considered."

"You know what they say about the senses. You lose one and it just makes the others sharper. Well, I believe that. Food tastes better now than it did when I was a kid. I can recognize just about anything by feeling it or smelling it. I've taught myself to do just about anything I need to do. It just takes me a little more time to do it than most folks."

"Do you have anybody to help you in your house?"

"Don't need no one. I got a routine, and I've taught myself to take care of everything in that routine by myself. Oh, my kids do come by from time to time and offer to do things, but you know what? They just end up moving things around and throwing me off. I know they want to help, but I do a lot better when they're not around."

I look at my phone and see we're just a few blocks away from Charles's sister's house. "I think we're almost there."

"Yeah, I've been timing it in my head and feeling the bumps in the road so I knew we were close. Take this next right up here, past the Family Dollar store. I'll call her and tell her to raise the garage for me."

We get to the house and I pull into the driveway. "Do you need any help getting out?"

"Naw, I got it." I watch this remarkable man as he feels for the door handle, opens it, remembers exactly where he laid all his belongings, gathers them, and steps out of the car.

"Charles, you have a great rest of the day. It's been a pleasure giving you a ride and talking to you."

"Pleasure's all mine. Now get on out of here." He flashes that grin again, then ambles into the garage, tapping his stick on the ground and feeling the wall with his other hand until he gets to his sister standing in the doorway.

The rest of that Saturday is pretty uneventful. Busy, but uneventful. That is, until about 9:00 p.m. when I get a call to pick up Tyrone. The address I see is in one of those proverbial bad parts of town, which means very little to me but worries my wife when she knows I'm there. I follow the route and stop in front of a small house on a hillside with a dirt yard and a steep broken concrete driveway. Rather than risk a tire puncture going up the driveway, I pull to the curb and make my call. Someone tells me that Tyrone will be right out.

When the door opens, I see a couple of young kids holding it open while an older boy, probably in his mid-teens, carefully maneuvers through the doorway in a wheelchair. Once clear of the doorway, he comes down the dirt yard toward me. He's moving slowly because it's pretty steep. If he were unable to check his speed, he would end up crashing into the side of my car. I wonder why in the world his younger brothers aren't helping him, so I dash around the front of the car to meet him halfway up the slope. "Let me give you a hand there."

"Thanks." His voice is flat and emotionless. As I grab the handles on the back of the chair, I notice that they are old, worn and rickety. Compared to Tyrone's wheelchair, Charles's things seemed like top-of-the-line equipment. I eventually get Tyrone just above the curb and beside the passenger door.

"How can I help from here?"

"I got it. Just open the door and I can get in."

I look at Tyrone skeptically, but once the door is open he does manage to swing himself in. I cannot help but notice that Tyrone's legs are completely limp as he does this.

"Does the wheelchair fold up? If it does I can get it in the backseat behind you."

Tyrone is staring at his phone as he responds. "Yeah, it folds up but let me do it. If you're not careful the back comes off and it's hard to get back on." I watch as Tyrone uses his right arm to pull the chair in position beside him, like he's no doubt done hundreds of times before. Using a technique I would have never figured out, he gets the chair folded as small as it will go so that I can slide it between his seat and the captain's chair behind him. "Wow, thanks. I'd have never gotten that done." Tyrone doesn't respond, preferring to keep checking his phone for texts and such.

I see from the GPS that I'm only taking Tyrone a few blocks, to another residential address. We ride in silence, but my mind goes back to the disturbing sight of Tyrone wheeling down the slope of his yard with no one there to help him. I wonder if there is a parent involved at his home. I wonder if those kids were his brothers. If so, why didn't they help him? I wonder how he ended up in that chair, without the use of his legs. Most of all, I wonder about his attitude and his station in life. I cannot tell if he is angry, sad, or just naturally quiet. One thing for sure, he has no interest in talking.

As we near the destination, I ask Tyrone if he needs to call someone to meet him and let him in the door. Only then does he look up and make eye contact with me. "No. I'm going to my aunt's house. They know I'm coming." It's as if asking for a little help is the farthest thing from his mind, and the minds of whoever happens to be at his aunt's house.

Mercifully, his aunt's house is on a flat lot and it's not far at all from the street. When I open my door, I hear loud rap music coming from the house, shaking the windows. It's late, and I'm about to drop this paraplegic young man at a house where heaven only knows what is going on inside. It's times like these that I wish I was empowered to make an executive decision and take Tyrone somewhere else. But I'm not, and I really don't know what's going on in the house, so I try to block the thoughts out of my mind. Instead, I pull out the folded wheelchair and begin to expand it to its normal shape for Tyrone. As soon as I start doing this, the back falls off of the chair. "Oh man, I'm sorry. I forgot that you said you needed to do this."

"That's okay. Here, let me see it." I push the chair beside Tyrone's seat, then pick up the back and hand it to him. Tyrone slowly puts the back of the chair on the metal frame and uses strands of frayed string to tie it in place. I'm sure the bolts and nuts that were supposed to secure it were lost long ago. He takes off his jacket, wads it up and places it in the chair seat, which has holes in it and looks as if it might not support his weight. His jacket does provide at least some cushion. Tyrone swings his body over the seat and drops himself down into it. Of course, there are no brakes on the chair, so it starts to roll away. But I grab the handles so Tyrone doesn't slip off the front. I feel like I'm powerless to help this challenged young man.

"Hope you have a great rest of the night, Tyrone. Be careful now."

Again, Tyrone doesn't respond. Instead he wheels toward the front door of the house and raises his hand back toward me as a parting "Thanks." I keep watching until he has opened the door and then closed it behind him.

Giving rides to people like Tyrone will drive home just how truly blessed people like me are. We complain about meaningless things and take for granted that we can do everything without difficulty. Eating, walking, driving, watching TV. I have no idea what's going to happen to Tyrone. All I know is that he's not enjoying the simple things in life like he should be able to. I continue to wonder what I could have done to help or to cheer him up. Probably nothing.

Then I remember Charles. Maybe if I can still find Charles's phone number in my cell phone, I can call him and give him Tyrone's number. If Tyrone needs a role model or a mentor, it's dang sure not me. It's Charles.

CHAPTER 7:

A TALE OF TWO STEVIES

We have a professional basketball team in our city that plays in a huge downtown arena. Like so many renovation plans and projects that cities come up with to try to revitalize a downtown area, our city placed the new arena right beside an entertainment district. The idea is that people will want to go to a game or a concert at the arena, then stick around downtown enjoying the nightlife and spending money at local businesses. It's a tried and true blueprint, one that countless cities have adopted in their efforts to bring people back downtown. My city did it about twelve years ago and so far it's been a success.

Uber knows all of this too. Each day and night, through the phone app, it designates certain areas in and around our city as hot spots. Pick up somebody in a hot spot and the driver earns a larger fare—the law of supply and demand. Capitalism is a wonderful thing. On most nights, the entertainment district is a hot spot.

It's the weekend and, on top of that, there's a college football bowl game in town and a pro basketball game tonight. Downtown will be hopping, especially the four-block entertainment district. If I want to maximize my rides and my earnings, my best bet is to hang around the downtown area and wait for calls.

My plan works pretty well and I'm having a very good night. It's about 9:30, still early for Uber drivers, and I've already given about twenty rides since early afternoon. I just dropped two young couples at a downtown restaurant. Before I can even get out of my parking space, my phone pings and I have another opportunity. Steve needs a ride. He is at an intersection on the west end of the entertainment district, just outside the door of a popular nightclub. I tap the app to accept the assignment, and in no time I'm motoring five blocks to pick up Steve.

The entertainment district is one street, for four consecutive blocks, all barricaded to traffic, so that patrons can walk the streets of that area without fear of being hit by a car. It's great for the businesses and the pedestrian patrons, but it's a nightmare for Uber drivers. Unless you know exactly where your passenger is, he or she could be anywhere in a four-block stretch. For this reason, Uber encourages riders to type in an exact address where they will be. It is my good fortune that Steve has taken the time to do this. He is at Third and Jefferson, on the west end of the district, and I know exactly where I can pull over to get him.

It's a five-block drive, but it's also an almost ten-minute drive because of all the traffic, both pedestrian and vehicular, that's downtown right now. The traffic volume, along with the one-way streets that seem to always be pointing the opposite direction from that which I need to go, makes my drive take much longer than normal. Eventually I get to the corner of Third and Jefferson, and I see a curbside spot that's at least partially open.

I may be blocking traffic a bit, but that's almost expected in this area. A young man is standing on the corner, looking down at his phone and then looking up at me. Aha! A sure sign I've found my passenger.

I roll down my window. "Are you Steve?"

"Yep. Are you my Uber?"

"At your service. Hop in."

Steve gets in the passenger seat beside me and extends his hand. "Thanks for picking me up. Man, it's cold outside!"

"Yes, it is. And there must be ten thousand folks walking around this area right now. Hope no one gets frostbite."

"Well, I won't. I'm calling it a night and going to my hotel."

I look down at my phone app and the destination reads "Holiday Inn Express" on Elm. I know that spot, so I won't even need to look at the GPS while I'm driving. I pull away and disappear into the traffic jam.

We drive slowly, and I eventually get my vehicle pointed in the right direction. Before long I have gotten out of the downtown area and am making good time. But then Steve looks down at his phone. Then he looks up, scans our surroundings and announces, "You know, I don't think you're going in the right direction. My hotel's not this way."

"Didn't you say it's the Holiday Inn Express on Elm?" I'm sure Steve must be from out of town and is just unfamiliar with the route I'm taking.

"Actually, I don't think I ever said anything about a destination. It's the Holiday Inn on Elm, but it's not an Express."

This presents a problem. Elm is a long street that stretches the length of the city, and it's very possible there are both a Holiday Inn and a Holiday Inn Express somewhere along the way. "Well the one my GPS is taking me to is about two miles from here."

"That's not it. Mine is within walking distance of where you picked me up. I just called you because I was too cold to walk."

"Then I wonder why the destination on my app says Holiday Inn Express?"

Just as I'm getting the word "express" out, my phone rings. Normally I don't answer phone calls when I'm taking a rider somewhere, especially when I don't recognize the number. I push "Ignore" on my phone and think nothing more of the call. I've got more important things on my mind; namely, where am I really supposed to be taking Steve?

"I'm sorry if I took you out of the way. Normally the destinations I see on my phone are exactly what somebody typed into their phone when they called for the ride. I don't know what caused a mix up this time."

Steve isn't worried. "Hey, it's okay. I'm just glad to be out of the cold. I figure it's worth a few extra dollars just to sit in these heated seats awhile."

"I know, but I still wonder why...." The phone rings again before I finish my thought. It's the same phone number that called a couple of minutes earlier. I figure it won't hurt to take the call, just in case it's an emergency. "Do you mind if I answer this?"

Steve doesn't care. He's just enjoying the ride, so I take the call. "Hello?"

The voice on the other end sounds confused. "Yeah. This is Steve. I think you're supposed to be giving me a ride. In fact, I think I saw you from a distance a few minutes ago but somebody else got in with you and you drove off. I hollered at you, but you didn't stop."

"I think you must be mistaken. Where were you when that happened?"

"The corner of Third and Jefferson."

Uh-oh. The Uber manual doesn't tell me what to do in a situation like this. I'm at least a couple of miles away from the entertainment district now, and it's beginning to look like I may have the wrong rider in my car. I look suspiciously at Steve—if that is really his name. Then I tell the guy on the phone, "Are you sure? I'm taking a guy named Steve to his hotel right now. That's who I was supposed to pick up."

"Well I don't know about him, but I'm Steve for sure. Is your name Jim?"

"Yes. Where were you supposed to be taken?"

"To the Holiday Inn Express on Elm."

Dang. He knows too much to be pulling my leg. My suspicion of the guy in my car is growing. Is he a freeloader? An imposter? I need to get this cleared up. "Sir, give me a couple of minutes to figure out what's going on, and I'll call you back. I'm heading back in your direction now, but I'm still a few minutes away."

Steve #2 is clearly perturbed. "So am I paying for this other guy's ride while I sit here in the cold?" That's a good question, and it sure seems like he probably is.

"I don't know. I'll have to figure it out, but don't worry. We'll make sure you don't do that, one way or another. Just let me get back to you." He hangs up.

Steve #1 has been listening to the conversation and has figured out what's going on. "Man, what are the odds of that? Two guys named Steve standing on the same street corner, both calling for an Uber at the same time!" He seems amused. I'm not.

"What did your phone app say your driver's name would be?"

He looks down at his phone. "Robert."

"I'm not Robert. I'm Jim. I wish you'd have asked me my name."

"Sorry." Steve #1 isn't sorry though. He's clearly relishing this conundrum.

My feeble mind tries to come up with a solution. "How about this. When I get back to the other Steve, how about I pick him up, take you to your hotel because it's close, then take him to his? You can give him cash to pay half the fare. It may not be a perfect solution, but at least no one is overcharged and both of you get back to your hotel."

Steve #1 mulls this over. "I don't know. You'd have to take me by an ATM because I don't have any cash on me." Of course he doesn't. I keep trying to come up with another solution, but my brain isn't cooperating.

"I'm going to call the other guy and see if something like that would be okay with him. I agree it's not right that he's going to be stuck paying for you to get your ride."

"But my ride was supposed to be short; just a few blocks. If he's going several miles from here, splitting the fare means I pay more than I should for my ride."

"Maybe I just take both of you where you want to go and then we let Uber figure it out."

Steve #1 likes this idea. "Works for me, as long as I get dropped off first."

Ten minutes later I'm back at the corner of Third and Jefferson. There's a sea of humanity milling about, but I halfway expect to see Steve #2 waiting for me. I pull over into the same spot as before and roll down my window. Seeing no one scanning a cell phone on the corner, I yell, "STEVE!" Everyone looks at me, but no one comes forward. I wait a few seconds and yell again. Still no takers. Getting more frustrated by the minute, I go to my call list and press the last number that called me, presumably Steve #2.

After several rings an aggravated voice greets me. "Hello!"

"Steve, this is Jim, your Uber driver. I'm here and looking for you. Can you raise your hand or something?"

"Don't worry about it. I got tired of waiting and just got a cab. I'm halfway to my hotel now."

Thank you so much Steve. But I guess I don't blame him. I sit there and ponder the time and miles I've wasted driving the wrong Steve in circles and doubling back to pick up somebody who isn't there anymore. Not the most efficient half hour I've experienced with Uber.

Meanwhile, Steve #1 is suddenly ready to get moving again. I think he senses that I somehow blame him for this whole fiasco, because when I turn to look at him he has dug his driver's license out of his wallet and holds it in front of my face. "See? Steve McKenzie. Man, this was just a crazy coincidence."

"Yeah, I guess so."

"So can I get to my hotel now?"

"Sure." I take Steve #1 to the Holiday Inn, a grand total of seven blocks from where I picked him up forty-five minutes ago. When he steps out, not knowing what else to say, he departs with, "Thanks. Kinda crazy, isn't it?"

"Yes, it is. I ended the ride on the app a while ago so it would stop charging the other Steve. Hopefully when he sees the charge on his credit card statement he'll dispute it. If somebody asks me about it, I'll tell them he shouldn't have had to pay anything." Without just coming right out and saying it, I'm hinting to Steve #1 that he should do something too. But Steve is either oblivious or giddy at his good luck. "Sounds good. Bye."

Steve #1 just got a free Uber ride. Steve #2 is going to see a charge for a ride he didn't get. Ultimately, I'll get nothing for all the fun of the last forty-five minutes.

Just another day in Uber paradise.

CHAPTER 8:

MISTER MANNERS

I'm about three weeks into my driving career. On the whole, it has been a pleasant experience. I now have over a hundred rides under my belt, so I can honestly say I've seen a lot.

Quite a few riders start conversations by asking me how long I've been driving and whether I like it. I've come up with a canned response that's both true and guaranteed to prolong the conversation. It goes something like this:

Rider: "So how long have you been driving for Uber?"

Me: "Oh, about three weeks now."

Rider: "Do you like it?"

Me: "I really do. It's like just about anything else in life. Nine-ty-five percent of the people I give rides to are nice people and there are no issues at all. But then there's that other five percent that, well, you know almost immediately there's just something not quite right with them."

The conversations always go on from there, because the rider wants details on the five percenters. After all, they're a lot more interesting than a story about someone you pick up, talk to for ten minutes about sports, and then drop off. People want to hear the scoop about the problem riders and how I handle them. So I always tell them about my experience with Greg.

I encounter Greg on a weekend night, in the trendy section of town with the late-night bars and clubs. When the notification hits my phone, I'm not far away and I see that Greg is at The Spotted Zebra, a popular place that serves good food and lots of drinks. No cause for alarm there; Greg might have just finished dining on the exquisite blackened grouper they serve at the Zebra.

Greg hasn't been dining. Greg has been imbibing. A lot. When I reach the Zebra and put the car in park, I see a very large man outside the front door, leaning on the wall. He looks to be every bit of six foot five, weighing in at a svelte three hundred pounds. And from the look of it, he is having great difficulty staying upright. Nevertheless, he recognizes me as the ride he has ordered. He staggers toward my vehicle. He lowers his head to look through the front passenger window at me and I smile at him. But instead of opening the door, he steps back to the rear door and opens it. He starts to sit in the captain's chair but stops. Then he steps back out, lowers his head toward me again, and raises a finger as if to say, "Just a minute." He hasn't said a word yet, but his appearance and gestures say all that needs to be said.

Greg walks back into the restaurant and so I sit back and wait. He's in the restaurant for a good five minutes. When he comes back out, he opens the front door and pokes that monstrous head at me again. This time he speaks.

"Where's my cell phone, man?"

It's not often that I'm at a loss for words, but for the life of me I can't come up with an intelligent response to his query right now. "Uh, I don't know."

"You had it. Now where is it?" He speaks these words very slowly, almost as separate sentences. I don't think that's because he's proud of his diction; I think it's because he's falling down drunk.

"Sir. I don't know where your phone is. You haven't even been in my car yet and I haven't seen it. Do you think you could have left it in the restaurant?"

Greg doesn't respond. Instead he starts opening my glove compartment, my console and just about anything else he can find to open in my car. "I know it's in here somewhere."

"Whoa! Please don't mess with those things. Sir, look, I don't know where your phone is. But I'll be happy to help you look for it. If you'll tell me the number, I'll dial it. We should hear it ring if it's in here."

Greg considers my offer and, seeing no down side, accepts. "555-3836."

I dial the numbers, knowing full well we won't hear a thing. I hear the phone ringing through my phone's speaker, but as I expected we hear nothing from inside the car. "It's ringing, sir. I don't know where it is but it's obviously not in here. Did you check outside the car? You might have dropped it when you were about to get in that first time."

Greg scans the area near the curb and sees nothing. His broken record greeting returns. "Where's my phone, man?"

I'm about to run out of rational things to say at this point. I look around and a small crowd has gathered outside the Zebra, watching us as we flail about in search of Greg's elusive phone. One of the onlookers steps forward. "What's going on, Greg?" Thank you. He's with someone and maybe they can help calm him down.

"This dude stole my phone." All eyes from the crowd swing to me. Am I really about to be fed to the natives? I direct my next comment to them.

"Look, I just pulled up here and he hasn't even gotten into my car yet. Do any of you know this guy? Maybe one of you can calm him down."

A petite young lady steps forward. "Greg, where was the last place you had it?"

Greg doesn't say anything. He just sways a second and then points into my car. I just shake my head at the crowd.

"Ma'am, I really think he must have left it in the restaurant. I can promise you it's not in here. I just called his number and we didn't hear anything even though it was ringing somewhere."

The lady seems convinced, for which I'm grateful. "Greg, honey, let's go back inside and look for it." She turns to me. "Do you mind waiting a few minutes? We need to get him home."

"Yeah, you do. I don't mind waiting, but please, he needs to know he's paying for me to wait."

"I ain't paying for shit!" Greg seems to have a problem with Uber's pay-for-waiting policy.

"Whatever. Please, just do what you need to do and then I'll drive him home."

Now, the prudent thing at that point would be for me to wait for them all to go back into the restaurant and then quietly drive away. But I've never been known to follow the prudent path, so I sit there and wait. The group, which numbers about six, stays in the restaurant for ten minutes, only to come back out phone-less. Greg still does not look pleased.

"I need my phone." Greg is now speaking to no one in particular, but he does glance at me as he says this. I respond by giving a pleading look to the young lady, as if to say "Help!" Thankfully, she picks up on this.

"Greg, sweetie, I'll ride with you to your house. Don't worry about your phone. We'll find it tomorrow. Somebody will find it and turn it in."

"Thank you. Can you make sure he gets into his house okay?"

"Yes. He's my brother. And he normally doesn't get like this, but he's had a lot to drink tonight." She helps Greg into the seat beside me and then takes her own seat directly behind him. We drive to his house without further incident and I notice that Greg is dozing. All things considered, that's probably for the best.

When we get to Greg's house, his sister shakes his shoulder and says, "Greg, we're here. Let me help you out and we'll get you in your bed."

Greg blinks a couple of times, realizes where he is, and starts to open the door. Out of habit, I'm sure, he reaches for his side pocket where he keeps his phone. Of course, there's nothing there. Greg's eyes widen. He slowly turns his head toward me. "Where's my phone, man?" I just drop my head in surrender.

Sister chimes in from the back, "Oh, good Lord. Come on Greg. Sleepy time for you." She helps her brother out of his seat, ignoring his incoherent mumbling, and steadies him as they walk toward his door. She looks back at me and mouths, "Thank you."

I just wave back at her. Before I drive away, I do hear Greg say one more time to no one in particular, "Where's my cell phone?"

I have no idea if Greg will ever find his cell phone. But if he does, I hope the first call he makes is to AA.

CHAPTER 9:

CATWOMAN

Self-awareness is a marvelous trait. Yet so many members of society are completely lacking in that area. Now before you accuse me of judging, I readily admit that I am guilty of being oblivious as well. Just ask my wife. She'll gladly tell you that I float along blissfully through life, totally unaware of the daily faux pas I commit. And I'm sure she's right. As the old saying goes, they aren't laughing with me; they're laughing at me (most of the time, I'm sure). So when I speak of society's lack of self-awareness, I know I'm either Pot or Kettle, but either way I'm calling someone black. But with apologies to Toby Keith, today I'm not talking about me—I'm talking about Catherine.

Nearly a month into this amusement park adventure called Uber driving, I've learned a lot. One thing that I had never been aware of, but I am now keenly aware of, is that many people use Uber on a daily basis. This may be to get to and from work, or to visit the store to pick up a few things. I've even had a few return riders, people I've picked up at the same time on different nights from their place of employment. I guess in a way they've become my "regulars."

Catherine isn't a regular, but apparently she does use Uber on an almost daily basis to run her errands. It's a relatively slow Wednesday night. I'm cruising a busy street in a hot spot area of town, but it's been nearly fifteen minutes since I've had a rider. That's not good for business, but it's a fact of life for drivers like me. We'd all love to have an endless string of riders awaiting our service, but most nights it doesn't happen that way. This night has been one of those nights, so I'm contemplating stopping and walking into a Starbucks for a cup of coffee. That virtually guarantees I will get a rider.

Just as the nearest coffeehouse comes into view, I get the notification from Catherine. She's not far away at all so the caffeine can wait—I've got work to do!

As it turns out, Catherine is at the neighborhood Kroger grocery store. Between Walmarts and Krogers, I have given lots of rides to folks with carts full of those wonderful plastic bags that won't stand upright or hold more than two or three items. Dropping those riders off at their destination almost always involves searching the floorboard for all the items that rolled out of the bags when they collapsed during the ride. I miss brown paper sacks....

I pull up to one of the two large entrance/exits to the store and see a lady with a cart full of bags who appears to be waiting on someone. She smiles at me, so I roll my window down. "Catherine?"

She looks at me with a confused expression. "No. How would you know my name anyway?" This woman has watched too many episodes of the X-Files.

"I'm an Uber driver and I'm supposed to pick up a Catherine here."

Ms. Conspiracy points to the other entrance/exit about thirty yards up ahead. "There's a woman who's been up there for a few minutes waiting on someone. Maybe that's your Catherine."

"Thank you." I move slowly forward as the first lady watches me suspiciously. I don't have the heart to tell her my Buick Enclave is actually an alien spaceship and she just missed out on a full abduction and probe.

The second woman is on the sidewalk just outside the door. She's bundled up because it's extremely cold outside, and I hope she hasn't been standing there long. Her cart is overflowing with bags, so I know immediately I'll need to get out and put the captain's chairs down to create enough room for her groceries. I roll down the window again. "Are you Catherine?"

"Yes. Thank you for getting here so quickly. Do you mind parking here by the curb while I unload my groceries?"

"Not at all. And please let me help you load your things so we can get you out of the cold."

"Thank you!" I wheel around sharply and pull beside Catherine's cart. Then I pop the back hatch door and get out to help Catherine load her things.

The first thing I grab is a huge bag of cat food from the bottom of the cart. It's one of those industrial size thirty-pound bags, one that would feed our cat Max for six months. Catherine doesn't need to be lifting things this heavy; she is petite and looks to be a few years older than me.

"Oh, thank you for getting that. I always need help with those big bags. Last week one of the sackers brought it all the way out to my car for me."

Red flag number one. Either Catherine is stockpiling thirty-pound cat food bags for the coming apocalypse, or she has an unusual need for the stuff.

"I understand. These things are pretty heavy." I toss the bag into the back of the car. "Here, let me get a few of those plastic sacks too." From the look of the cart, Catherine has probably twelve to fifteen plastic bags, all tied neatly at the top to prevent the spillage I normally encounter on trips like this one.

I grab about four sacks and although they are tied, I can still see most of the contents of them. The bags I'm currently carrying are filled with canned cat food and cat toys. Second red flag.

Our combined efforts get the cart completely empty in three trips, with the last item being the forty-pound bag of cat litter I wrestle into the small remaining space in the back of the SUV. I push the empty cart into the nearby cart corral, and off I go with Catherine and her cache of feline products. The trip to her house looks to be only about a five-minute drive.

Under all the coats, wraps and scarves, Catherine is bright eyed and eager to talk. She seems very pleasant, so we immediately begin a conversation about where we are from and how we ended up where we are now. Somewhere early in the conversation I mention that I grew up on a farm in central Arkansas. This piques Catherine's interest.

"I have family over in Arkansas. Have you ever heard of a little community called Imboden?"

"Sure have. In fact, we used to have a state trooper in our town whose last name was Imboden, and he always said his family was originally from there and the town was named for them."

"I'll bet he knows my cousins then. I think you mentioned you grew up on a farm. What did you have there?"

"Rice, soybeans, winter wheat. And when I was really young my granddad had cattle."

"Really? Did you grow up having to milk the cows?"

"Oh no ma'am. They were beef cattle."

"Oh my word! You mean you raised them to just slaughter them?"

The flagpole is now replete with crimson. I consider correcting Catherine to make sure she understands that first of all, I didn't raise the cattle, and second, those T-bone steaks she just passed on aisle twelve had to come from somewhere. But discretion is the better part of valor, so I steer around her comment. "Well, we only had them until my granddad passed away, then my dad sold them all because he was too busy in the fields to take care of them. So were you raised on a farm too?" A smooth segue if there ever was one.

"No, I'm a city girl. You know, I just can't understand how people can eat meat. Have you ever read up on how the cows are treated and how they are just slaughtered after they're sold?"

"No, but I guess they have to end up on our plates somehow." I'm dying here, and in desperate need of a new subject. "So I take it you are a cat person and not a dog person?"

"Oh, I'm both. I just have a soft spot in my heart for animals, and this time of year when it's so cold I adopt a few. I figure it's the least I can do to keep them from freezing to death outside."

"Well that's commendable. I've always been a dog person, but a couple of years ago we inherited a cat from our daughter when she moved into a new place that didn't allow pets. He's grown on us, and now he's king of the castle."

"Yes, they will definitely grow on you. Cats are special!" Sorry, but I'm leaving that last comment alone. I'm not sure I really want to hear what her elaboration would entail.

"So which house is it?" I'm on her street. As always, I want to make sure I don't pass her house due to the occasional inaccuracy of the GPS within the Uber app.

"It's the one on the right with the carport light on, just ahead." I see the house, which is small but neat. The carport has no car parked in it. "My car is in the shop and I'm not sure when I'm going to get it back."

"Well, just call us whenever you need to go somewhere. We're here to help." I turn into her driveway and stop just short of the carport. "Let me help you with your things."

I'm not sure of the protocol for Uber drivers handling a rider's grocery bags once the destination is reached. It seems a little forward and intrusive to carry the bags into her house, unless she specifically asks me to do so. Catherine allays my concern, though. "If you don't mind, just put everything here in the carport by the door. I'll carry the small things in. The heavier things just stay out here anyway."

I turn the car off, pop the back hatch, and begin the task of unloading Catherine's things. I cannot help but notice the background noise emanating from her home, which for all the world sounds like someone strangling a herd of cats. It's unnerving. Catherine doesn't seem to notice it at all. In fact, she's not ready to end our visit.

"Let me show you the things I've got here for the cats." Oh yes. Please. She directs me to the opposite corner of the carport, where five sturdy little houses are carefully arranged. They look like huge dollhouses, obviously custom constructed by someone and not bought at a pet store. "I get these from a friend who builds them as a hobby. They've got insulation in the walls, carpet on the floor, and vinyl that drapes down to cover the opening. The feral cats that come here at night stay in them, and it keeps them nice and toasty."

"Wow. I'm sure they appreciate that. How many might you have at any given time?" One of the golden rules of being a trial lawyer is to never ask a question of a witness that you don't already know the answer to, but I'm genuinely curious so I break that rule with Catherine.

"Oh, probably fifteen. They're built to accommodate up to four cats each, but usually only three will stay in one."

Fifteen feral cats. In addition to all the cats meowing in the house, the number of which shall hopefully remain unknown.

"You're really doing your part to keep the cat population good and healthy."

"Thank you. I just can't bear the thought of them shivering in the cold at night." I nod my head as we shiver in the cold.

"Well, I think that's everything but the litter bag. Do you want it to stay out here too?"

"Yes. I go through a bag in just a couple of days." Then Catherine proudly adds, "I clean the litter boxes three times a day for them."

My mind is aflutter with images of those cat people you see from time to time on the news. The ones that neighbors eventually call the cops on because of the unsanitary conditions. The ones that the reporters tell us had ninety-six cats in and about their property. Oddly enough, Catherine's property—at least the outside—is very neat and sanitary. I pray that the inside is as well, but it would probably take a herculean effort for that to be the case.

I need to pick up another rider, so I prepare to end my time with Catherine. "Is there anything else you need before I go?"

"No. I think that's everything. Thank you so much for your help, and it's really been a pleasure visiting with you. Some of the Uber drivers I've encountered don't seem to want to talk much, and I've always felt so uncomfortable when we ride for ten minutes and no one says a word."

"Well, I hope you've had a positive experience tonight, ma'am. Don't forget, whenever you need a ride, just contact Uber and they'll send someone for you, even if it's not me."

"Oh, I know. In fact, I'm sure I'll be taking another ride tomorrow night. I'm just about out of dog food."

Mercy.

CHAPTER 10:

FRAT BOY BLUES

I was fortunate growing up to have parents and a grandmother who would not tolerate rude behavior or impoliteness. The need to be polite to people was instilled in me at a very young age. Now, I don't deserve a gold star or blue ribbon for this, because most people are the same way. And I cannot claim that I never let frustration get the best of me and stray from the standard my folks demanded.

Figuring out why being polite matters is pretty simple. Just consider how people act toward you. If they treat you with rudeness or contempt, the encounter leaves you in a foul mood, and you are well on your way to having a bad day. But if you are treated with respect and in a polite manner, it brightens your disposition. A wise boss once said that you should treat the janitor with just as much respect as the company CEO. I think this is a pretty good rule of thumb.

This seems especially true to me when I'm driving. I have no idea what's been going on with my passengers, especially those who aren't very talkative. For all I know some of them are silently dealing with a crisis or with pressure at home or at work. A little kindness goes a long way. Even if what I say to them turns out to be the only nice thing they've heard all day, well at least they did hear that.

As I tell people all the time, ninety-five percent of my riders seem to follow the same rule that I do. The rides are pleasant and enjoyable. But there will always be those five percenters. I'm guessing they didn't have parents or grandparents like I did.

Heathcliff is a five percenter. I don't know his real name and I seriously doubt that it's Heathcliff, but the name evokes images of snobbery and entitlement, so it's what I'm calling the guy. I encounter Heathcliff on a Saturday night, during prime time for yuppy partying. It's a busy time, but also a risky one. Seems that the majority of unpleasant rides, infrequent as they are, originate during that time and from this neighborhood.

I'm in the trendy area tonight because I know it will be full of young revelers in need of rides home. Most of the trips aren't long. But they do keep me close to the area, so I'm giving lots of rides—albeit inexpensive ones. A group of four has just been dropped off at a lounge with authentic blues being played inside. As I sing along in my car to the familiar tune, my phone pings. The request is from Lauren, and judging from the address she's right around the corner. Less than a minute later I'm there, waiting on Lauren to emerge from the bar.

Lauren does emerge, with Heathcliff. I know I've written earlier in this book about the dangers of stereotyping, but full descriptions of what I'm seeing now are appropriate and necessary.

Lauren is a pretty young lady, dressed to the nines and no doubt the product of a lifetime of expensive orthodontic and cosmetic care. Stated another way, she looks like the typical southern belle during a night on the town.

Heathcliff is all frat boy. It's winter but unseasonably warm tonight, so he's decked out in an IZOD polo with the collar popped, pressed khakis and topsiders. I'm sure there are argyle socks under those khakis too; I just can't see them. To top off his ensemble, a sweater is tied around his neck. And his hair is spectacular; blonde and blown to perfection with nary a hair out of place. I'm sure Heathcliff would say it's all the product of good breeding.

Lauren identifies herself and I invite the couple into the Enclave. Heathcliff immediately breaks the ice.

"Dude, what's with these bucket seats back here?"

I glance at him in my mirror. "They're standard in this model. I think they're pretty comfortable. Most folks seem to like them."

"I can't even sit next to Lauren. I feel like I'm in the cockpit of a plane."

"I'm sorry. There's a back bench seat if that works better for you."

"So you're telling me I have to bend over double to climb back there and then bunch my knees up to my chest just to sit? No thanks."

"Suit yourself." I glance to the other seat. "Are you all right back there?"

Lauren looks longingly at her beau. "Yes. I'm good."

We drive a ways and Heathcliff speaks to Lauren in a low voice, but not so low that I can't hear him clearly. "What's this guy's name again?"

Lauren whispers to him, "It's Jim, I think."

I guess the fact that Lauren is not one hundred percent certain leads to the next nugget from Heathcliff.

"Hey Uber. Are you sure you know where you're going?"

Misidentification aside, I look down at my GPS. "1227 Royal Oak Drive. Isn't that where you're going?"

"Yeah, but this isn't the best way to get there. It's not even close. Do you know this town at all?" He lowers his voice again and turns to Lauren. "Uber's trying to run up your fare."

Despite the slow boil of my blood, I ignore the comment. "Sir, I'm just following the GPS directions that the app gives me. If you have a better route that you want me to take, tell me and I'll follow it instead of this."

"Would have been nice to know that before we got in this neighborhood. We're in it now, so you might as well go ahead and keep going this way." Which is exactly what I intend to do.

We drive silently for a while, then Lauren and Heathcliff talk some more. Thankfully I'm not the topic, but it becomes pretty clear after a while that Heathcliff is quite full of himself and that none of the people they were with earlier in the evening measure up. The more he talks, the more it's apparent that Heathcliff gets his jollies downgrading other people. And then he hits a nerve.

"Hey Uber. What's a guy like you make doing this?"

"Well, you can call me Jim if you like, but I generally..."

"Okay Uber."

The interruption and disparagement make me cringe. Oh how I wish my grandmomma could hear this spoiled punk. She would have corrected him one time, then cut a fresh switch from the pear tree in her back yard the next time. "...I generally make somewhere between fifty and a hundred dollars a night if I drive from 5:00 until 11:00 on a weeknight. Weekends I may make quite a bit more, depending on how long I drive and if there's anything going on in town like a ballgame or a concert."

"That's not bad, Uber. But this is a pretty nice ride on that kind of money. Must be a rental, right?" He glances at Lauren and snickers a condescending snicker.

"Oh, this isn't my only job. I have a day job too."

"Really? What's that?"

"I clean up after the elephants at the zoo." Sometimes I can't help myself when the fruit is hanging so low.

"Hope you showered before you started driving tonight."

I take a deep breath to help calm my urge to say something I might regret later, then I respond. "Actually, we've had this car about a year. Second Enclave we've had. Liked the first one so much we got the 2017 model when we traded in last December."

Heathcliff has lost interest in the sound of my voice because he's talking to Lauren again before I finish my explanation to him. "Hey Uber, can you stop at this store up here? We need to pick up something." The store we are about to pass is a wine store, and since it's on the route and won't require a significant detour, stopping at the passenger's request is encouraged by Uber.

"No problem." I pull into a parking space and watch as Lauren and Heathcliff go into the wine store.

I can see through the huge glass windows that they go down every aisle, study countless bottles, and finally settle on one. The whole process takes close to fifteen minutes. Meanwhile, I'm just waiting, and waiting, and waiting…

"Thank you." Lauren says her first real words to me as they get back into their personal limousine.

"No problem at all. Are we ready to get going again?"

"Yes sir." Lauren sure seems polite, which makes me wonder why she tolerates Heathcliff's boorish behavior. I halfway expect her to apologize for him, but so far that hasn't happened.

"Hey Uber, guess how much this bottle of wine cost."

"Well, let's see. It's not in a box and it doesn't appear to be from Boone's Farm, so I'll say it must cost more than $7.99."

"It cost over a hundred dollars, Uber. Bet you've never seen one of these before."

"Actually, I have. My wife and I have been to Napa a couple of times. We didn't buy any of the expensive stuff, but we took the winery tours and tasted a lot of it. To be honest with you, I can't really tell the difference between a ten-dollar wine and a hundred-dollar wine."

"That's not surprising."

I wonder if this is how he treats the servants at home?

When we get to the house that I assume is Lauren's, I stop and wait for them to get out of the car. Instead they continue to sit.

"What are you doing, dude?" I guess if Uber is my name, then dude is my nickname.

"Is this not your house?"

"No. It's that one." Heathcliff points to the very next house, every bit of fifteen yards from where I'm parked. The one with the driveway full of cars.

"This may be as close as I can get, but I'll go somewhere else if you want."

"Go past the driveway. That'll be closer. We aren't supposed to have to walk to the house. Uber says you're supposed to take us right up to the house."

"Okay, whatever. Here, I'll pull up past the driveway." I do, and we are almost exactly the same distance from the front door as we had been before I moved, but to Heathcliff this is more acceptable.

"That's fine, Uber. We'll take it from here."

Lauren leans up to me and says, "I think there's a way I can leave a tip through the app, isn't there?" Maybe a nice tip will be her way of apologizing for her brat of a boyfriend.

"I think you can. I'm not that familiar with...."

"You're not supposed to tip, Lauren. That's the beauty of Uber. You pay the fare through the app and you don't have to do anything else. They don't even expect a tip. Right, Uber?"

If there is any justice in the world, this guy will be driving for Uber within six months after his trust fund is bled dry. "Actually, you can do what you want. I think you can leave a tip by using the app, but you certainly don't have to, and it's totally up to you whether you want to. Doesn't make any difference to me either way."

"See Lauren? We're good to go!" They exit the car and walk into the large house to my right.

Where's a pear tree when you need one?

CHAPTER 11:

MAIL-ORDER BRIDE

I've been to this place before, and I know it may not be the right place. My Uber app's GPS has led me to an apartment complex in one of the nicer areas of the city, but it backs up to some trendy shops and restaurants, separated by a wall. The last time I was here, it turned out that my rider was at one of those restaurants and it took me a good ten minutes to finally figure it out and pick her up. That happens sometimes. You learn to deal with it, but it's still frustrating. My first clue then had been when the directions led me to the wall and the target on my map – meaning the specific location of the rider—was on the other side of it. Deja vu is my companion now, as I creep closer and closer to that wall.

I know people live in these townhouses. I see vehicles parked in the spaces in front of them, but for whatever reason the app confuses the commercial side of the huge brick wall with the residential side. I'm looking for Tatyana, and right now it's anyone's guess whether she's sitting in her apartment on this side of the wall or finishing a nice meal on the other side of it. Sitting in my vehicle, staring at the wall in front of me, I decide to call and find out. After several rings, someone answers.

"Hello?" The voice is feminine, with a heavy accent that sounds Russian or Eastern European.

"Hi. Is this Tatyana?"

After a short pause, she says, "Yes. Who is this?"

"This is Jim, your Uber driver. I think I'm close by, but I can't tell exactly where you are. I'm in the apartment complex, but it's pretty big. I don't know if you're in one of these buildings or if you're even in the complex."

This time the pause is longer. "Not apartments. Townhouses. You see townhouses?" Her English is broken and the words come out slowly, sounding for all the world like they are being spoken by the female villain in a James Bond or Austin Powers movie.

"Yes. I called them apartments but I guess they are townhouses. Are you here, or am I in the right place?"

"I'm in townhouse. Come to back?"

Now it's my turn to pause. "Do you mean the back of the complex, or the back of one of the townhouses?"

"Need to leave now. Hurry please."

"Ma'am, I'm here, or at least I think I am. But I need to know which building you're in and when it's dark outside I have a hard time seeing the numbers on the buildings. Right now I'm parked against the curb near the big brick wall at the back of the complex. Am I close to your apartment?"

"No apartment. Is townhouse." This woman has something against apartments.

"Right, right. A townhouse. I just need to know which one." I keep staring at the GPS, which indicates I am right on top of where I'm supposed to be.

"I will come outside." That's good. I pride myself on great service, but even I can't pick up someone in their living room.

"You parked where?"

I look around to see if there is another landmark I can give her. "I'm in a white SUV parked against the curb by the big brick wall on the north end of the complex. There's a street light just above me."

Pause. "What is 'Es You Vee'?"

"It's a cross between a car and a truck, sort of like a station wagon on steroids." I realize as soon as I say this that I will confuse her even more. "Just look for a large white vehicle; a Buick Enclave."

I wait, and I see from the app that Tatyana is now being charged wait time, which is just a few cents but who knows when she will find me. Or if she will find me. Just as I'm wondering what to do next there is a tug on one of the rear doors. It surprises me and I whip around, ready to subdue the armed intruder. But it's Tatyana.

"This is Es You Vee?"

"Uh, yes. Are you Tatyana?"

She smiles and nods affirmatively, then slips into the captain's chair behind the passenger seat. In the captain's chair behind me, she sets a large duffel bag that appears to be full of clothes. I tap the phone to indicate I've picked up my rider, and I see that she is going to the entertainment district downtown, a good twenty minutes away. Twenty minutes is a long time to drive in silence, so I decide to engage her in conversation.

"Did I pronounce your name right? Is it Tatyana?"

"Yes."

"That's a beautiful name. Are you from Russia?"

"Yes. Actually, Belarus. It used to be part of Russia."

"I thought I recognized the accent. Are you visiting or do you live here?"

"I live here for two years."

I glance in the mirror at Tatyana. She is young and very pretty, but she sounds sad. Maybe she's homesick, or maybe it's just the accent. "Do you like it here?"

She glances out her window. "I like it when I live in New York City. I not so much like it here."

"I'm sorry. How long have you been here?"

"Six months. I'm from big city in Belarus. I have friends there and friends in New York City. I have no friends here."

That's understandable for sure. I'll bet she gets lonely and I wonder why she is here, in a place where she has no friends. She probably doesn't want to talk about it though. We drive for a few minutes. Soon I overhear her talking to someone on her cell phone. I don't want to eavesdrop, but in the silence of the vehicle it's hard not to hear what's being said. Hearing it is not hard; understanding it is something else altogether because some of the conversation is in English and other parts are in Tatyana's native language. The conversation lasts only a couple of minutes. Tatyana seems irritated when the conversation ends. Maybe I can take her mind off of things. "Would you like to listen to some music?"

"No. Please just drive me to club."

"No problem." I continue to drive but apparently Tatyana isn't through with whoever she was talking to on her phone. She calls him back. This time things get heated. After just a few seconds Tatyana is yelling into her phone, a mix of broken English and whatever Belarusians speak. The substance of the conversation is in Belarusian. The curse words are pure English.

"I GO HAVE FUN TONIGHT!" "I FEEL LIKE PRISON-ER IN THIS F*****G CITY!" "YOU HAVE YOUR PARTY, NOW I GO HAVE MINE!" These are only a few of the things I can understand very clearly, interspersed with the Belarusian being screamed into her phone. Gradually, the words slow down and are replaced with uncontrollable sobbing. The cursing continues though.

When you are sitting in a driver's seat, it's hard to be invisible. But right now I try with all my might to be as inconspicuous as possible. This is really uncomfortable. Who is this young woman? Who was she just fighting with over the phone? Is she connected to the Russian mob? What's really in that duffel bag? Just how fast will this Enclave go?

When Tatyana has composed herself a bit, she speaks. "I'm so sorry for this. I no want to bother you with problems."

"Hey, it's okay. I hear all kinds of things all the time." I gesture toward the floor beside her seat at a box of Kleenex I keep for times just like this. "Do you need a tissue? You can use as many of those as you need."

"No. I'm fine. I just need to go to party place." She's still sobbing, but there's a hint of anger in her voice as well. Then she reconsiders and reaches for the tissues. I hear her wiping her eyes and her nose, and she says, "Thank you. I no mean to be so much trouble for you."

"You're no trouble at all, but I have to ask, are you gonna be all right?" I look back at her because we're stopped at a red light. She nods that she will be.

"It's my husband. He treat me like prisoner. He go out all the time and I never know where. He come home and say nothing. But I cannot leave! I try to go have fun and he go crazy! He say he send me back to Belarus! He buy ticket for plane tomorrow!" She starts sobbing again.

"Uh, gosh, I'm sorry. Is he from Belarus too?"

"No. He is from Turkey. He meet me in New York City two years ago and we get married. He always nice in New York City, but then he move us here and he just want to be mean all the time now. He say he kill me if I go out without him!"

Okay, that's serious. Do I call 911? Do I take this poor lady to a women's shelter? Is she even legal here? I've got a predicament to ponder.

"Where do you want to go?" I look at my phone and we are only a couple of minutes from the drop off point downtown. "Do you still want to go to the club you were planning on going to?"

"I don't know. I call friend. He will help me." I thought Tatyana had no friends here, but now's not the time to quibble with her. She dials up another number and pretty soon she's talking to someone again, this time completely in a foreign tongue. The conversation is short, and thankfully it's relatively civil. She taps me on the shoulder and speaks to me again. "He want to talk to you."

Were we moving right now I think I would probably just drive straight into the river; thankfully another red light has us stopped. I glance over my shoulder and Tatyana is thrusting her phone under my nose. Uber doesn't pay me enough to have conversations like this.

"Uh, who am I going to be talking to?"

"Nadir. He is friend and he will help me. He is friend of my husband too, but he look after me and keep me safe."

"So this isn't your husband that wants to talk to me?" I pray this isn't a KGB agent tracing the call.

"No; this is Nadir. Please talk to him. He tell you where to take me."

I reluctantly take Tatyana's cell phone. For a moment I hold it and stare at it like Clark Kent handles kryptonite. "Hello?"

"Sir? Is this Uber driver?"

"Yes, it is. Who am I speaking to?

"My name is Nadir. The girl in your car is a friend. She's troubled. Bring her to us. We will take care of her."

Nadir's English is much better than Tatyana's, but he is obviously not American either. If he's truly wanting to help her, I'm good with that. But I do have a few concerns; namely, who is "we"? And what does he mean by "take care of her"? AND WHAT'S IN THE DUFFEL BAG?

"Is her husband with you? She seems to be having a fight with him, and I just want to make sure she is okay."

"No, he isn't here. He is out of town. This happens a lot. You bring her to me and she can stay the night here. She will be better tomorrow. We just don't want her to get hurt. You know?"

Yeah, I know. But I also know I don't want to be the getaway driver on the periphery of an international incident. I need more convincing as I make my U-turn and put downtown in my rear-view mirror. "Well, if I take her to you, I'll need an address so she can change the destination on the Uber app. As of right now I'm being paid to take her downtown." I'm not really that concerned about the extra payment, but I also don't want to spend the rest of the night driving this lady around for nothing.

"I will text her the address and she can give it to you. And there is no need to do it through Uber. I will pay you in cash when you get here." No doubt in unmarked bills.

"Okay. But are you sure this is what I should do?" I look back at Tatyana in the mirror, lines of black mascara running down her cheeks.

"Yes. She will be fine with us. You know. Young couples. They fight. They cool off. They make up. They love each other again. Kids."

I'm tempted to turn to Tatyana and ask her if she wants me to drive her to some faraway place. That might be the best way to insure her safety, but it might also open me up to charges for kidnapping or interstate transportation of stolen mail-order brides. And I might have the Russian mafia on my tail too. The options aren't that attractive, so I figure I'll roll the dice and drive Tatyana to Nadir. I just hope we aren't meeting them in a cornfield out in the country.

"I spoke to your friend. He wants me to take you to where he is. Is that what you want?"

Between sniffles Tatyana nods her head. "Yes. Nadir is nice. He protect me. He try to keep my husband and me from fighting. I stay with him lots."

"Okay then, we'll go to Nadir's place." I instinctively look down at my app and then realize it won't tell me where to go. "I think he's going to text you the address and you'll need to let me see it on your phone."

Just as I say that, Tatyana receives the text and hands me the phone again. I'm relieved to see an address I recognize, in a good part of town where there will be witnesses in case I get shanked.

On the twenty-minute drive to Nadir's place, I try to take Tatyana's mind off of her dilemma. "So are you a student here, or do you work somewhere here?"

Tatyana smiles. "I have degree from university in my country. I work there as nutritionist, but I no work here. My husband no allow it. He make me feel like prisoner all the time."

"Would you like to try to find work here?"

"No. I want to go back to New York City and see friends. I tired of this place."

"Have you tried to make friends here? Maybe other young people who live in your apartment complex?"

"Townhouse. No. No one friendly there, except to my husband. I think he tell them not to talk to me. I think they spy on me for him."

"I'll bet if you just get out and start talking to people who live around you, you'll make some friends. This really isn't a bad place, but I'm sure it gets lonely when you don't know anyone."

"The thing is, I am adult. I have education. He cannot tell me what to do." She starts to cry again.

"Please, it's going to be okay. Is there anything I can do? I mean, other than drive you to your friend's house?"

"No. My problem. I must deal with it."

"Do you really think he is going to send you to Belarus on a plane tomorrow? And isn't that really what you want anyway?"

"He won't. He will lock me in townhouse again. And he will go out and have fun party." For a moment I fear she is going to tell me to turn around again so she can go to the club and have fun herself. Fortunately she doesn't.

"You do realize you could contact people about protecting you, or getting you away from your husband and making sure you're safe from him. I mean, the police, lawyers, women's shelters..."

"No. I go to Nadir. He protect me."

We keep driving until we reach a gated apartment complex adjacent to a golf course. Nadir might be from another country, but he's obviously done fairly well for himself. These are luxury apartments and there is a security guard in a little hut beside the gate, something for which I am thankful at the moment.

"Excuse me, but do you know the code to open the gate? Or do I need to talk to the guard and see if he will let us in?"

"No, we not go in. I see Nadir, next to truck parked by street."

I look in the lot outside the gated apartments and see three large men leaning against the bed of a nice late model pickup truck. No weapons are in sight. The smallest of the three begins to walk toward us and motions for me to roll down my window. Saying a prayer for protection, I comply.

"I am Nadir." The man extends his hand through the open window and offers to shake mine. I reciprocate. and I can tell by the look in his eye that he is harmless. "Thank you for this, and I am sorry for the trouble. Tatyana is … what you call it … drama queen?"

"I'm just glad she seems to be okay now. I was worried for a minute there." As I say this I see Tatyana run to the other two men and give both a big hug. She's smiling now, talking calmly to them. "Do you have to do this a lot?"

Nadir laughs. "About once a week. Her husband is not a bad man, but he gets frustrated and yells at Tatyana. She threatens to run away. Then she calls me. She will be all right tonight."

"Well thank you for intervening. I wasn't sure what to do and I didn't want to leave her somewhere in the condition she was in."

"You do the right thing. You bring her here." Then, just before I begin to roll the window up, Nadir digs into his pocket. "Here. I hope this covers the trouble. Have a nice night."

"You too, sir." I drive away and stop down the street in an open spot. The crumpled bill in my hand is a fifty-dollar bill, which makes this a seventy-five dollar ride when the original Uber fare is added.

I pull back onto the street, in search of Russian mail-order brides to rescue and drop off with Nadir. I think I'll check in townhouses.

CHAPTER 12:

SURF'S UP!

As I've mentioned, having a nice roomy vehicle has its advantages when driving for Uber. Larger groups can ride with you, airport passengers with lots of luggage want you, and on occasion someone with an oversized item in need of transportation will specify a large vehicle. The fare for a bigger vehicle like mine is a little higher, which means more money for me when I see the "Uber XL" designation on my phone screen from time to time.

Tonight I'm all over the map. Uptown, downtown, midtown and all the suburbs. It's a Friday night and it's busy. Most of the trips are short, so my fares are small, but there are lots of them. A notification comes in and I see it is in a very nice residential neighborhood. Great! Good tippers maybe.

My passenger is Robert. As I pull to the side of the busy thoroughfare, I see that the house is luxurious. Robert obviously does quite well. Maybe he and his trophy wife are going out on the town, and have called Uber like responsible people should do before embarking on a night of revelry.

When Robert emerges from the house though, he doesn't look like I imagined. For one thing, he looks to be in his early twenties. Okay, maybe this is Robert's son. For another thing, he's carrying something huge. I hope it's not his dinner date because if it is, she's in a body bag. Robert walks to the back of the Enclave and tries to find the button that will open the hatch. Instinctively, I open my door to go do it for him, almost losing the door in the process as a car speeds by in the next lane and lays on the horn to alert me to my carelessness.

"Oops, my bad. I didn't see him coming. Here, let me get that for you."

Robert is still feeling for a button and has laid the huge mystery item up against the side of the Enclave. Whatever it is, it's taller than my SUV. "Thanks. You may have to put the back seat down for this to fit." I survey the situation as the hatch slowly rises and nod in agreement.

"You're Robert, right?"

"Yes, and you're Jim?"

"Yep. We're both in the right place. Do you need a hand getting this thing in?" I'm dropping the seats down and I'm still not sure his bag is going to fit.

"I don't think so. It's actually pretty light. Besides, my boss is pretty particular about who handles it." I step back and watch as Robert carefully turns the item on its side and begins to slide it ever so slowly across the cargo space and between the captain's chairs. It's still not all the way in, and he keeps sliding it forward. Finally, the front of it bumps up against the dashboard. There's still a good six inches of item sticking out the back.

"Maybe if you tilt it up a little the front can go up over the dash until it touches the windshield." I don't have any straps or rope so tying this thing to the top isn't an option. Robert takes my suggestion and the end of the item moves in a bit more. It's going to be tight, but it looks like the hatch door may shut. I push the button and it slowly comes down, eventually clicking and locking. We're in!

Robert and I walk around the SUV and get in our respective doors. He sits in the seat beside me and immediately begins pushing buttons on his phone. I hit the button on my own phone to indicate I've picked up my rider, and I see that we're headed to the Westin Hotel downtown, about fifteen minutes away. "The Westin downtown? Is that where we're going?"

Still rapidly pushing buttons on his phone, Robert replies, "No. I'm going to change the destination. We're actually going to go to the FedEx shipping terminal south of the city."

"Okay. I can go ahead and get started in that direction, but do change the destination on your app. Otherwise mine will think I don't know where I'm going."

"No problem." Just as he says that my phone pings and I see that the destination has been updated to the FedEx terminal. It's also about a fifteen-minute drive, but in the opposite direction. I check my mirrors, wait for a couple of cars to pass, and pull back into traffic.

Judging by the shape of the nylon bag that covers Robert's item, I'm guessing that it's a surfboard. I mean, what else could it be? The front tip is wedged under my rear-view mirror and the back tip is pushing hard on the bottom of the back hatch, and the shape suggests surfboard. My curiosity demands confirmation, so I strike up the initial conversation with Robert.

"So I'm guessing this is a surfboard?"

"It is. And it's a very expensive one." Robert has still not looked up from his phone and he doesn't seem too interested in talking. That has never stopped me before.

"Are you headed somewhere for a competition or something? Vacation on the west coast maybe?"

"No, it's not mine. It belongs to my boss."

"Oh. Is your boss at the Westin then?"

"No. He's in San Diego. He flew out there yesterday and for some reason the airline wouldn't check his board. So he left it with me and told me to figure out a way to get it out there to him."

"I see. That's strange. I know you can check all kinds of things and most airports have a special area where you go to pick up your oversized items once you land."

"I don't know what the problem was, but my boss didn't have time to argue with them. So he called me and told me to handle it."

"He must have a lot of faith in you to give you that kind of responsibility."

"I'm his personal assistant, but what that really means is that I'm his gopher, to be quite honest with you. But he pays me pretty well and he's promised me a promotion sometime this year."

"That's good. So what does he do?"

"He's a day trader."

"Really? Does he own a brokerage firm or something?"

"No. He just got filthy rich on his own about ten years ago and now he just plays around."

"So if he doesn't do anything, and he's promised you a promotion, what will you be promoted to?" I don't want to rain on this kid's parade, but it seems that all the stops on his career path may include the word "gopher."

"I'm not sure. Actually, it's going to be a raise but he keeps calling it a promotion. And he's pretty well known around town, which is good because he's told me he could be a great reference if I ever want to go work for somebody else."

"I'm sure he would be." I shift gears and return to the task at hand. "So back to the surfboard. Is he a competitive surfer?"

Robert laughs for the first time. "No. He's a beginner. He has a lesson scheduled for tomorrow afternoon with some legend out there, and I've got to get this board to him by tomorrow morning."

"Can't he just rent one there? Or buy another one if he's that rich?"

"No, you have to know him. He bought this board for like thousands of dollars. It's custom made. If he doesn't have it, he'll cancel his lesson and it'll be my head when he gets back."

"Got it." I look at my GPS and see that we're just a minute from the terminal. I wind through the gated entrance to a little hut with a security guard eyeing me suspiciously. "Hi ma'am. I'm an Uber driver and my friend here has a package he needs to have shipped tonight."

The security guard is unimpressed. "You have to go to one of our retail locations to do that. This is where we load the trucks."

Robert leans over to further explain. "I was told I could take this here and it could be marked for delivery on the dock."

"Well, I don't know about that. Who did you talk to?"

"I didn't get her name, but it was someone I contacted through your website. She directed me here and told me to go to Dock 73 because there's a truck there that is going to the airport with cargo going to San Diego later tonight."

The security guard thinks for a minute, then goes back into her hut and reemerges with a clipboard. "Sign on this sheet, then go all the way to the end of the terminal and take a left. You'll circle around to the back and you'll see the docks. The dock number is above each one."

We both say "Thank you" in unison and follow her directions. Once we get to the docks, with hundreds of Fed Ex trailers backed into them, we start reading numbers. Eventually we get to the one with a large "73" over it, so I stop. There's no one in sight. I turn to Robert and say, "Do you know what you're supposed to do?"

"Not really. If you don't mind, just wait here and I'll look around." Robert gets out of the vehicle and disappears between the rows of trailers.

Twenty minutes later Robert reappears. He doesn't look happy.

"What happened?"

"I found a guy and he told me I'm in the wrong place. He said the lady I spoke to on the phone didn't know what she was talking about. Everything they load on the trailers has to come from one of the retail locations."

"What are you going to do?" I don't want Robert to lose his gopher job for this mystery man, but I also don't want to drive to San Diego tonight.

"He said there may still be a couple of retail places open if we can get there quickly." He looks at his watch. "It's a quarter to eight; I'll have to check and see what the hours are at the locations close to us."

"I'll do what I can to get you there in time if you find one open." Robert is working his phone furiously again. A few seconds later, he strikes gold.

"There's one on Lancaster that says it's open until eight. How far is that from here?"

"I'm not sure. Enter the address in your phone app and it will automatically re-route me. When it does that, it will tell me how far away we are."

Robert types in the address and the new route appears on my phone. It says we are fifteen minutes away. And away we go.

I haven't gotten a speeding ticket since I've been driving for Uber, and I really don't want to get one now, but by golly, I'm on a mission. I maintain a steady speed that's only about eight or nine miles per hour over the posted limit, figuring that's the leeway the police will give, and I pass under at least four yellow lights that are in the process of turning red. Miraculously, we don't rouse any blue lights. With three minutes to spare we pull into the FedEx store. Robert runs through the door. From my seat I can see him explaining his dilemma to the young man behind the desk. The conversation lasts three minutes. It ends with the two of them walking back to the door. Robert exits, and the young man pulls out his key and locks the door behind him. The surfboard is still in my vehicle.

"What happened this time?"

"The guy said all their cargo for overnight shipment left here three hours ago. I could leave the board here, but it wouldn't go out until tomorrow afternoon. My boss wouldn't get it until late tomorrow night, and that's too late."

"Oh man, I'm sorry."

"He did have one suggestion though. He said there is actually a small retail store at the airport that stays open all night. He checked the computer and there's still one more plane bound for San Diego tonight. If we go to that location, we might still be able to get the board on that plane."

I don't even bother to tell Robert to change the destination on his app again. I just wheel back into traffic and make a beeline for the airport. Once we're comfortably on our way I say, "Get the address so I'll know where to go. The airport grounds are huge, so I'll need to know exactly where we're going. "More furious button pushing from Robert, and a new address appears on my phone. "Okay, got it. We'll be there in twenty minutes."

I follow the route my GPS has given me, and pretty soon the airport is in sight. Robert is drumming his fingers on the dashboard and I know he is nervous as a cat. I look down at my phone and see that we're getting closer and closer and closer….

When the GPS shows that I have arrived exactly on the spot, I look up. We are in a parking lot—a dark, massive parking lot surrounded by a fence. There's no retail store in sight. In fact, there nothing in sight except for rows and rows of cars. There's not even a security guard hut this time. I turn to Robert. "Are you sure this is where we're supposed to be?"

"It's the address for the airport location that the website shows."

"Well, what do you want to do?"

"Let me call FedEx again."

I can hear his conversation, and it's not long before I hear that the retail location at the airport was closed several months ago, that the last plane bound for San Diego is about to take off, and that there's no way he can get the surfboard to San Diego by tomorrow afternoon. Robert's head drops as he ends the conversation.

"Man, I'm sorry."

"Hey, it's not your fault. But I need to call my boss and tell him. He's gonna go ballistic."

"Well, where do you want to go? I mean, I've got to take you somewhere."

"I guess head back toward the Westin downtown. That's where he originally had me going."

"I guess I'm wondering why there, since you were trying to ship a surfboard and I don't think there's a Fed Ex or UPS location at the Westin."

"He's got a lady friend who's been staying there this week and is leaving in the morning. I'm supposed to check on her to see if she needs anything before she goes to bed tonight."

"Was that your house or his that I picked you up from earlier?"

"That's his. He sent me there to get his board."

"But his lady friend isn't staying at his house?"

"Uh, no. I doubt his wife would like that too much."

Sometimes conversations end abruptly. This is one of those times. I drive toward the Westin as Robert dials his phone. I know he dreads making this call and I'd prefer not to hear it, but there's no way I can avoid it. The conversation turns out to be short, and thankfully civil. When Robert ends the call, he laughs.

"So is everything okay? It doesn't sound like he fired you."

"No, he didn't. And yes, it's okay."

"So what about the board? How are you going to get it to him?"

"I'm not. He said he canceled his lesson when he landed at the airport, and he just forgot to tell me."

What a jerk. Poor Robert has been running all over the city trying to conjure up a miracle for this guy, and all the time he didn't need his surfboard anyway. A short call or text would have been nice. Heck, he's been on my clock for almost an hour and a half now. I try to think of a way to console him as I pull under the canopy that covers the entrance to the Westin.

"Well, it's certainly been an experience. I have to say you're taking this well."

"It's just a typical day working for him. Things like this happen all the time. I've learned to just deal with them and move on."

"That's a good attitude. Maybe that raise and promotion will be waiting on you when he gets back to town."

"Maybe. But he's out there for a week so I won't know for awhile."

"Well, go take care of his lady friend. I'm sure she'll put in a good word for you with him."

"Yeah, she'd better. She's my aunt."

CHAPTER 13:

JOSIAH

I know that the more entertaining stories are the ones involving drunks, illicit rendezvous and madcap adventures that take me all over the map. But that's not every night, and it's not what the majority of Uber rides entail. Most are uneventful, bordering on mundane. Some are forgotten as soon as the ride ends. Occasionally, however, someone leaves a mark, even if you're not sure why or what kind of mark it is. Someone like Josiah.

It's early in the evening, still light outside, and I'm in a neighborhood not far at all from my house. It's a golf course neighborhood, but not one of those million-dollar-home neighborhoods. The houses are all very nice, but on the smaller side and owned by middle class folks. Even though I'm only a mile or so from home, I don't think I've ever been down this particular street before. I get to the house with the street number where Josiah is supposed to be, so I roll into the driveway and put the Enclave in park.

After about a minute I call Josiah's number. Someone answers the phone on the third or fourth ring, and a very feminine voice says, "Hello?"

"Uh, yes, I'm calling for Josiah. This is his Uber driver, Jim, and I just wanted to let him know I'm here in the driveway."

"This is Josiah. I'll be out in a minute." Maybe it was a bad connection, but the voice sure didn't sound like a guy. I continue to wait, and in a couple of seconds the front door opens. Out steps Josiah.

The young man walking toward my vehicle appears to be less than five feet tall, thin as a rail, with a buzz-cut haircut and clothes that look to be three sizes too large for him. It's hard to say how old he might be, but I'd guess late teens. If I had to compare him to anyone in my mind, I'd have to say the hillbilly boy who played the banjo in the movie Deliverance. He walks all the way to my vehicle with his head down, opens the front door and sits in the seat beside me. Then he looks up, smiles broadly, and extends his hand to me. "Are you Jim?" It's the same feminine voice from the phone, and he appears to have a lisp.

"Yes, I'm Jim. And you're Josiah?" I shake his hand, fearing almost immediately that I've crushed his fingers since there is no firmness to his shake at all.

"I am. It's a pleasure to meet you, Jim. Thank you so much for coming out here to give me a ride." Yes, Josiah clearly has a speech impediment. "Ride" sounds like "wide", and "pleasure" sounds like "pweasuwe." I can certainly understand him, but his lisp-like speech is glaring. I try my best to ignore it.

"Well, giving rides is what I do, and it's a pleasure to meet you too, Josiah. Let's see where we're going." I touch my app to indicate I've picked up my passenger, and the destination appears.

It's Playhouse on the Square, which is a repertory theater in the mid-town area. "Oh, the Playhouse. Are you going to see a play tonight?"

"No. I'm going to class."

"Really?" I cut myself off because I'm afraid I'm sounding condescending. I change my tone to make sure I sound genuinely inquisitive. "What type of class are you taking there?"

"Oh, I take a dancing class and an acting class."

"Cool! Is it, like, for college credits or are you just taking the classes because you enjoy them?"

"Oh I'm not in college right now. I take these classes at the Playhouse because they're fun. I'm kind of an artistic guy. I paint too."

"Well you must be talented then. I have trouble with paint-by-numbers."

Josiah misses my lame attempt at humor. "Oh I'm sure you have talents too. Do you like to dance?"

"No, not really. I don't have much rhythm."

"Maybe if you took a class you'd learn to love it. I find I can really express myself through dance."

"Well, I did actually take a ballroom dance class when I was in college, but it wasn't because I really wanted to take the class. The girl I was dating at the time signed up for the class, so I did too, just so I'd have a class with her. Then, as luck would have it, we broke up and I was left in the class with nobody to dance with. And I was horrible at it."

"That's funny. I'll bet I could teach you to dance."

Okay, now things are getting weird. "Thanks, but my plate's kind of full right now. Plus, dancing's just not my thing." I decide to change the subject. "How about the acting class? Do you like it?"

"It's okay. I'm thinking about taking a writing class too. Do you think I should?"

"Well if you enjoy writing, yeah, I'd say go for it."

"Do you like to write?"

"You know, I suppose I do. Sometimes when my business at home is slow, I'll just start writing to fill in the time. I guess it's therapeutic in a way."

"I write a lot of poetry. Especially when I'm down and I feel like giving up. That's when I write some of my best poetry."

The more Josiah talks—and he's talking a LOT—the more I sense that he doesn't have any friends. I can picture other kids making fun of him when he was younger, and I have no idea if he's still school age or not. He would be the poster boy for bullying based on his size, appearance and voice. Right now though, he seems overjoyed that he's found somebody to talk to who is actually listening and talking back with him. I want to think that he's truly talented, but my mind keeps wondering how he can participate competently in either a dance or an acting class. With that voice, and his physical challenges, it just seems . . .

"What do you mean when you say you feel like giving up?" I say that instinctively, not really thinking about how intrusive the question is.

"Oh, just no hope. Wondering why I'm here. I get depressed a lot."

Now I've done a complete 180, and instead of wondering whether this kid can dance a lick, I'm concerned that he's a social misfit who may have suicidal thoughts. Maybe I'm overreacting, but I suddenly begin feeling compassion for this young man.

"Listen, I'll bet your poetry is pretty incredible. And what about your paintings? What do you like to paint? Landscapes? People?"

"Oh, just faces. People I see."

"Have you ever shown your paintings to other people?"

Josiah's eyes light up and he turns his head toward me. "Just my mom. But I'd like to have a showing at a gallery someday. If I have one, would you come and see my paintings?"

"Absolutely. I'd consider it an honor."

"If I can set it up for sometime in the next couple of months, could you help me?"

"Uh, I don't know how I could help, but I'd come if I can."

"Oh, that was so rude of me to ask you that. Here you are being all nice, and I ask you something stupid like that."

"It wasn't rude or stupid. It's just that it's outside my area of things I know about. And we're gone a lot, traveling and such. I'd hate to commit to do something and then find out I'm not going to be here."

"You wouldn't like my paintings anyway."

"Now how can you say that? You may be the next Van Gogh and nobody knows it yet. Until you let someone look at them, how can anyone know whether they'd like them or not?"

"I don't know. I know you're just being nice to me."

I sigh a big sigh and look at Josiah since we're stopped at a red light. "Josiah, I'm not the smartest guy in the world, but one thing I do know is that it's a lot easier to be nice to somebody than it is to be rude or mean. At least it is for me. And if you think I'm just being nice to you, you're right, but only because I can tell you're a nice person and you deserve people to be nice right back to you."

Josiah pauses and then says, "My last few Uber drivers who brought me here didn't say a word to me the whole way. I almost dropped out of my class because I started dreading the ride to the Playhouse. In fact, I almost didn't come tonight. If you hadn't called me, I wasn't going to come out the door."

"Well, I don't know what those other drivers' deals were, but all I can say is they missed out. Look, we're here and we've talked the whole way. You're an interesting guy, and it's been a pleasure bringing you to your class. Go in there now and dance up a storm."

"It's acting tonight."

"Whatever. Go act up a storm."

Josiah smiles and extends that hand again. I take it and squeeze a little more gently than I did the first time. As we're shaking hands, Josiah looks up at me and says, "I'm going to say a prayer for you tonight, Jim. I hope God watches over you and keeps you safe." "Prayer" comes out as "pwayew", but that only serves to drive home his sincerity. The door closes and Josiah walks toward the Playhouse door with his head up. He's an odd-looking and odd-sounding little fellow by society's standards, but I think tonight he's going to be all right.

It's only now that I notice the lump in my throat as I watch him disappear into the building.

CHAPTER 14:

SOMEBODY'S DAUGHTER

It's Saturday morning. My wife is spending the weekend with her mother out of state, and there's a music festival downtown. This could be a really nice payday, but to make it a huge day I need to start as early as possible. I've got nothing else to do, so after I get the pets to do their business and get them fed and watered, I start my day. I look at my watch: 8:45 am. I doubt I'll get many calls for the first couple of hours, but you never know. The early Uber driver gets the passenger.

My phone vibrates and pings before I even get out of my neighborhood. When I tap the app, I see that my first rider of the day is about two subdivisions over from me. Man, it's going to be a good day! It takes me less than five minutes to get to the address where I will pick up Vince.

Vince lives in a very nice neighborhood, where the houses are large and overpriced. Maybe he'll be a big tipper, starting my day on an even bigger note. I drive slowly down his street, past the

111

row of two-story houses with three-car garages on huge lots. His house is on the right, and when I see his number on a mailbox I maneuver the Enclave into his driveway. Something's a little odd though.

At the end of the driveway, standing in the open garage, are a large man who appears to be in his mid-thirties dressed in shorts and a t-shirt, and a much younger female dressed in a, well, I'm not quite sure what it is. It looks like what flappers wore back in the Roaring 20s, or what you might see on a street corner in a city's red light district. Neither look particularly happy.

The man motions for me to get out to speak to him, so I stop the Enclave about ten feet away and walk up to them. The man speaks first. "Jim?"

"Yes, hi. Are you Vince?"

"Yeah. Look, I'm not the one getting the ride; she is." Vince gestures toward the young lady who has yet to raise her head to make eye contact with me. "I assume the address she gave me is a good one."

"That's fine. I'll confirm it when we get going." I turn toward the young lady. "Are you going home?" She silently and slowly nods her head.

"One more thing. You probably will need to help her into her house. She's pretty drunk. Here, I know you get paid through your account, but here's a little extra for your trouble." Vince hands me a twenty-dollar bill and turns to walk into his house. The young lady still keeps her head down and says nothing. I realize I have yet to get her name.

"Okay, you want to get in the car? I'll check where we are going and I'll get you there as soon as I can." She nods again and takes a step toward the passenger side of the Enclave, but then she stumbles. She's wearing high heels, but she's wobbly enough on her own. I instinctively move quickly to catch her before she falls, and for the first time she looks up at me. I finally see her face, and it's heartbreaking.

This young lady cannot be more than eighteen years old. Her face is caked with poorly applied make-up and mascara that is running down her face with her tears. Her reddish hair is matted and dirty, and her bright red lipstick seems to cover half her face. She might be pretty, but you'd never be able to tell. Finally she says her first words to me. "Where are we going?"

By now I think I've figured out what's happening here. This young lady, whatever her name is, attended a party at Vince's place Friday night. She wasn't a guest though; she was the entertainment for the evening. I don't want to think about what that might have entailed.

I open the rear passenger door and help her into the seat. She seems to be close to passing out, so I quickly grab the seat belt strap and snap her into her seat securely. Her dress, which is gold sequined and barely covers her crotch, has ridden up so high that I cannot get the lap belt to go across it. Instead it is pressing into her bare legs and it looks uncomfortable, but I'll be darned if I am going to try to tug the bottom of her dress down lower.

"Is that uncomfortable? Can you readjust your dress or the belt?"

"It's fine. Where are we going?"

"Well, let's see. It says here 5221 Oakhaven. Is that right?" I know that area. It's not a good one and it's more than forty-five minutes away. Oh boy.

The young lady nods her head affirmatively, so I close her door, walk around the front of the Enclave and prepare myself to drive her home. I adjust the rear-view mirror so that I can see her, just because I'm not sure of her current state of mind. "Mind if I ask you your name?"

"Mandy."

"Mandy? That's a pretty name. Barry Manilow wrote a song about you."

She looks quizzically at me. I realize there probably aren't too many eighteen-year-olds who would know who Barry Manilow is, much less one in Mandy's current condition. Rather than probe, I decide to just turn on the radio and start the ride. I back out of the driveway and we embark on our journey.

About five minutes into the ride I hear sobbing. I glance in the rear view and Mandy has her head down, crying loudly. I turn around because I'm getting genuinely concerned. "Are you sure you're okay?"

Mandy nods without looking up. "I'm sorry. I'm sorry."

"There's nothing to be sorry about. I just want to make sure you're okay. Is there something I can do?"

Mandy shakes her head no. "I just need to get home."

"Well that's where I'm taking you. Do you need a Kleenex?"

"No." Then she looks up at me. "I'm sorry."

"Please, don't apologize. I'm just taking you home."

The sobbing slows and Mandy tries to smile. "You're so nice."

I'm no psychologist, but I'm pretty sure that Mandy has had a tough upbringing. And I'm also pretty sure she's on something. Her facial expressions and her reactions aren't what you would expect from a stable, sober person. Mandy stares out the window and suddenly her demeanor changes. "I don't think this is the way home."

"Really? The GPS says it's down the interstate about fifteen miles, then I get off near the airport and drive south for a while. Is that where your house is? If it is, this is definitely the best way to go."

"Where are we?"

"We're on the loop, headed toward the south side of the city. Isn't that where you live?"

"Uh huh. Are you taking me home?"

"Yes ma'am. I'm taking you home."

Mandy smiles. "Yeah, that's what I need to do. I just need to go home." I can't tell at this point if she's laughing, crying or oscillating between the two. She appears to be an emotional wreck. Then she puts her hands on her stomach and makes a pained expression.

"Are you going to be sick? Do I need to pull over?"

"No. I'm fine. I'm sorry." She's definitely crying again now.

"I can go through a drive-thru and get you something to eat. Would that help?"

"No. I just need to go home. Will you take me home?"

"Yes. I'll get you home."

We drive for a few minutes without conversation, but I keep checking on Mandy in my mirror. She's crying quietly now, occasionally mumbling to no one. I remember Tatyana, the Belarusian mail order bride I had driven a few weeks earlier. Mandy is different though. Tatyana was just a young lady in a strange country who felt trapped in a relationship. Mandy is a young lady who has probably never really had a chance, spiraling downward in a dangerous way. I wish I could help her somehow.

"Do I need to pay you?" I'm still not sure Mandy knows where she is or where I'm taking her. I pray that it really is her home.

"No ma'am. The man you were with when I picked you up has already paid for your ride. You just need to help me in a few minutes by pointing out your house and making sure I get you to the right place. Can you do that?"

Mandy nods. Then she says for about the tenth time, "You're so nice." I wonder if there is anyone in Mandy's life who is truly nice to her.

As always at times like this, my conscience butts into the situation. I know I'm supposed to give Mandy a ride, make sure she gets where she needs to go safely, and go on about my business. But I can't leave well enough alone. "Mandy, do you mind if I ask how old you are?"

She pauses before answering. "I'm nineteen." I can tell she isn't telling the truth.

"The place where I'm taking you, is that your parents' house?"

Mandy shakes her head. "I stay with Dex."

"Is he your boyfriend?"

"He's a guy who helps me out and takes care of me." I'll bet.

"Is it going to be okay for me to drop you off there?"

"Yeah. I just need to go home."

It starts to rain, pretty hard, and I'm about to the point where I'll exit the freeway and start looking for street signs. As I already knew, the farther I drive into this area the worse the neighborhoods get. I do have an umbrella in the car, but it's a small one designed for only one person.

"Is this your street? I just turned on Oakhaven. Do you recognize where we are?"

Mandy peers out the window. "Yeah, this is right. It's that house on the corner there."

I pull slowly in front of a tiny rundown house with a bare yard that's already under water. There's a chain link fence around it and a gate that appears to be ajar. I pull to the curb, put the SUV in park, and turn around to Mandy. "Why don't you let me help you into your house?"

"I need to go in. Dex will be waiting for me."

"It's storming. At least let me walk you to the door with an umbrella."

Mandy seems to ponder this for a second, then she nods her head. I get out of the Enclave, grab the small umbrella and go around to open her door. She's fumbling with the seat belt latch, having no success getting it to open. I reach across and undo it for her, and in between sobs she says one more time, "You're so nice." I help her step out onto the curb and I raise the umbrella so it covers her. She takes one step and then says, "Wait, I need to get my purse." She bends down over the captain's chair to reach her purse on the other side, and I cannot help but notice that she isn't wearing underwear. The bottom of her dress is literally at her waist, but she either doesn't know or doesn't care. I look away as quickly as I can.

"Here, get back under this umbrella. And show me where you go in the house."

We walk down the broken sidewalk, through the gate, and across the submerged yard to the front door. The umbrella is keeping Mandy somewhat dry, but I'm getting soaked to the bone. When we reach the door I ask, "Do you have a key?"

"Yeah, in my purse." She rummages through her small purse and finds the key. "I don't think Dex is here."

"Okay, well then, if you can get in the house, I'll need to be going on. Are you sure there's not something I can do?" I have no idea what I could do, but asking seemed to be the right thing to do.

Mandy shakes her head no, then for one of the few times during our encounter, she looks at me. When she does, she breaks down and begins sobbing uncontrollably. Instinct takes over and I reach out and wrap her in a bear hug. She hugs me back, tightly, and we just stand there in the rain hugging. It's a pitiful sight I'm sure.

After a minute I step back and tell her to go in the house because she's getting soaked. She nods and disappears through the doorway. I walk back to the car and sit down, soaking the nice leather seats and the carpet with my waterlogged self. I look back at the dilapidated house where I just dropped off Mandy. Who knows what goes on in there? Is Dex a pimp? Do other unfortunate girls live there too? Is there food in the house?

As I drive away, the thought that keeps creeping into my mind is a simple one. Mandy is somebody's daughter. It's enough to make me want to go back to Vince's house and punch him in the face.

CHAPTER 15:

FULL CIRCLE

It's May. I've been driving for Uber for about six months. Our daughter's wedding is just a couple of weeks away, and the money I've made driving has certainly come in handy. On top of that, my real work has picked up and I'm finding myself driving less and less after hours. It's been interesting in many ways, and I may still continue to drive on occasion, but I do think that after the wedding I will take a break, maybe even all summer.

I'm out tonight—a Friday night—knowing it may be my last night to be an Uber driver for awhile. Am I heartbroken about this? Not really. It has served its purpose and I've met some really interesting and memorable characters along the way.

Tonight has been a typical Friday night so far, with the usual suspects seeking my services to get them from point A to point B. I've had some college students, some white-collar folks, some night shift workers going to their job, and some out-of-towners going from the airport to hotels. It's been steady, but now it's close to midnight and I'm about ready to call it a night. I've been downtown for awhile so I set my app to accept ride notifications that are only on my way home. Rarely do I get a rider when I have the app on that setting, but you never know.

Sure enough, tonight is one of those rare nights. Before I get on the freeway that will take me home, I get a notification that Jillian needs a ride and she is going in the same general direction as I am. Great! The address where she is looks familiar. I think I've picked up someone there before.

Lo and behold, I have. Jillian is at the same restaurant/club/bar where I picked up Amy and her band of millennial misfits my first night driving for Uber. I begin to have flashbacks—ear-splitting music, mouth throw-up, Kanye, rude behavior. Surely history isn't about to repeat itself.

As I pull to the curb in front of the yuppie establishment, my fears are allayed. There are very few people there. The outdoor hostess actually smiles at me as I illegally park in front of her station, and I see no belligerent groups waiting for a ride home. Instead, I see a solitary woman standing near the street corner, phone in hand, watching me as I arrive. She's dressed in business casual and has a professional look about her. This will be a breeze.

"Jim?" She bends to peek in my rolled-down passenger side window.

"That's me. Are you Jillian?"

"I am."

"Front or back; your choice."

"I'll sit in the back, thank you." She slides into the captain's chair behind the passenger seat and buckles herself in. "This is a very nice vehicle," she says as she surveys the interior of the Enclave.

"Thanks. We like it." I look down at my phone and see Jillian's going to one of the nice suburban communities about twenty-five minutes away. I'm sure she's headed home after a late business dinner or an after-work night out with friends. "Ready for the weekend?"

"Yes, it's been a long week. Say, can we stop at a drive-thru somewhere on the way to my house? I need to get something to eat."

"Be happy to, but at this hour I don't know what we're going to find open other than convenience stores. Is that okay?"

"No, I'd rather get something substantial, like a burger. There's a Wendy's about halfway to the house that we'll pass. Stop there."

I look down at my watch instinctively, knowing that chances are slim we will find a fast food restaurant still serving after midnight. "Okay, we'll give it a shot." We commence the drive in silence.

About fifteen minutes later I pull in to a darkened Wendy's with no sign of life in or around it. Oh well; it was worth a shot. I turn to speak to Jillian. "It's closed. What do you want to do?"

Jillian is agitated; more so than the typical person would be at finding out Wendy's isn't open. "What time is it? I can't believe they're already closed!"

"It's about twenty after midnight. I really don't think we're going to find anything open except convenience stores."

"Well I have to have something to eat. Please find one quickly."

What is it with this woman? Is she diabetic and on a strict eating schedule? I don't want to be blamed for her suffering some sort of reaction, so I simply say, "Yes ma'am. I'll stop at the next place I see open."

"Please do."

I drive further, off the route, in search of a clean convenience store. It's going to be a few minutes before we find one, and I hope Jillian's okay back there. I keep thinking to myself, "I've been driving folks around for six months now and I've managed to avoid any major incidents. Surely I can make it through one more trip." I look down between my seat and the console where a few makeshift barf bags have sat undisturbed for the past six months.

Jillian is whimpering in the back seat. She's doing it quietly, but I can definitely hear it. "Are you okay ma'am? Do I need to call someone for you or take you somewhere else?"

"No. Just get me some food and I'll be fine."

"Are you sure you don't need me to pull over for you? Are you about to be sick?"

"NO. I'm FINE. I just need some food."

We reach a stoplight and I turn to check on Jillian – just as it happens. After all those trips; after all those conversations with people asking me if it had ever happened; after all the near misses. Jillian spews.

Yes, Jillian throws up, right before my eyes. And it's unmistakable. She's not diabetic. She's just drunk and up to that point had been good at hiding it. But there is a silver lining. Jillian manages to throw up into her lap and not on my seat or my floor. For that, I guess I am grateful. But the smell is enough to turn my own stomach, so I immediately roll down all four windows. Of course, Jillian begins to cry.

"Ma'am, there are some tissues in a box on the floor, but I don't have any towels or anything. I'll get some for you when we stop at the convenience store."

"Oh, I don't need anything to eat anymore. Just take me home." She's crying, but for some reason she seems to be blaming her predicament on me. As if I were the one who drank all night on an empty stomach and then refused multiple offers to pull over. She's embarrassed. I know this because I hear her mumble under her breath, "I'm so embarrassed."

We drive the rest of the way in total silence, as I fight to keep from being overcome by the stench and she sits with her legs clenched together, vomit pooled on her dress in her lap. The two of us are quite a sight to behold, I'm sure.

As I approach Jillian's house, she says, "Take me to the door by the garage." I comply, and almost before I can stop the car she opens the door and gets out. As soon as she steps out, I hear a sickening "splash" on the concrete driveway. Better there than on my floor.

There won't be a thank you. There won't be a tip. As Jillian scurries into her house, I know there will only be the lingering smell of rum drinks and the lingering image of said rum drinks exiting Jillian's mouth at an accelerated rate of speed. It's not a pretty mental image, but fortunately the Enclave was spared.

I'm ten minutes from home. Uberville has been a nice place to visit, but I've concluded I wouldn't want to live there. Like all places, you have to take the good with the bad. From remarkable blind passengers to surfboard-toting personal assistants; from cat loving women to families headed to Chuck E. Cheese; from illicit affairs to terminal cases of the hiccups—you see it all from the driver's seat.

And as I pull into my own driveway in the wee hours of Saturday morning, I'm grateful for the experiences and for what I've learned along the way. To the good people of Uberville, thanks for the memories.

Oh, and to Jillian, I've got the number for a great dry cleaner.

Acknowledgements

Good things often come from unlikely sources. When I looked into driving for Uber and Lyft, my sole intention was to make some extra money so some unexpected family expenses could be covered without dipping into savings. Writing a book about my experiences was the farthest thing from my mind. But from almost the first night, I sensed that I would encounter people who would leave a lasting mark on me. Rather than let these folks fade from my mind, I decided to memorialize their stories, which over time became *Tales from Uberville*. All names have been changed to protect identities, but that is about all that has been changed. All the people described in this book are very real, as are their stories.

Any first-time writer has doubts about what he is writing. In those times of doubt, the encouragement of friends and colleagues is invaluable. Several individuals have, over the years, read some of my writings and have provided that encouragement.

David Fuqua, a friend for thirty-five years, has encouraged me to seek publication of my writings on more than one occasion. His confidence in me has been one of the reasons I am still writing today. Ditto Bill Haltom, a superb writer in his own right, who is always there to give me an attaboy when I've written something that he enjoys. There are many others, too many to name, but to all who have ever complimented me on my writing, know that your encouragement feeds my perseverance.

Last, but certainly not least, I want to thank my family, for letting me be me.

Bio

 Growing up in the small farming community of Lonoke, Arkansas, J.D. Lawson wanted to be a professional football player. That didn't work out. Instead he became an attorney and a mediator. Today, he practices law and mediates in western Tennessee and throughout Arkansas. In his spare time, when not following his beloved Arkansas Razorbacks, he officiates high school football games in the Memphis area. He lives in Lakeland, Tennessee with his wife Vicki, their two dogs Roxy and Riley, and their cat Max. He has four children and two grandchildren. *Tales from Uberville* is his first published work.

31720552R00076

Made in the USA
Middletown, DE
07 January 2019